RAMAYANA

RAMAYANA
INDONESIAN WAYANG SHOW

by
Sunardjo Haditjaroko, M.A.

PENERBIT DJAMBATAN

ISBN 979 428 040 2

Revised edition of 'LIVING SHADOWS'
by the same author

With Illustrations by R.M. Soehatmanto
Printed by: Hastama

Contents

Author's preface

Full appreciation depends on detailed knowledge. Therefore it is clear that, before one nation can come to fully understand and appreciate another, it must be well acquainted with the mentality of the foreign people, and, for practical purposes, the quickest way to acquire such an understanding is to study the customs, the institutions, the religions and the art of the nation in question, for these are the things that best illustrate the mentality and the way of life of each individual nation.

There is no need to emphasize the importance of international understanding in the present world. It is however worth noting that up till now, the exchange of such cultural information between East and West has been rather one-sided. Great efforts have been made to westernize the East, but little has been done to easternize the West.

This publication is a humble attempt to establish a healthy two-way traffic, by acquainting non-Indonesians with one of the most popular and captivating stories from Indonesia's rich cultural store. Though the independence of our country is fairly new, our culture is old. We trust therefore that, in our small way, we too can offer something to the cultural understanding of the modern world.

It should be pointed out here that the story is actually the Indonesian version of the famed Indian classic 'Ramayana'. Coming centuries ago from the snow-capped Himalayas to the warm plains and snowfree mountains of Indonesia, the original epic has of necessity undergone many drastic changes, affecting not only geographical and personal names, but also the story itself. This of course is readily understandable when we realize that on its arrival on Indonesian soil, the Indian

'Ramayana' encountered a vigorous, already blooming indigenous culture which in the course of time reshaped and remoulded it into its present form. In point of fact, the epic is now deeply rooted in our national heritage and forms part and parcel of our national life. This is proved by the existence of the three characteristically Indonesian forms in which the epic manifests itself, namely: the 'wayang kulit' which is a shadow-play ('wayang' and 'kulit' mean respectively 'shadow' and 'leather'), the 'wayang orang' which is a type of opera ('orang' means 'men'), and the 'sendratari Ramayana' which is a type of ballet, all of which enjoy great popularity.

The outhor feels deeply indebted to Dr.H.R. Dodd, Mr.A.N. Donovan and Professor Bernard Lott for reading the manuscript.

Jakarta, 1st January, 1970

Introduction

A great deal has been said or written about underdeveloped or developing countries or the third world, and one has invariably has in mind just one isolated aspect of the overall culture of these countries, namely the economic phase. Admittedly, these materially less privileged countries have a stagnant economy—low GNP, low per capita income, precarious communication facilities, pot-holed roads, etc. etc. But an impartial observation of the present stage of the development of the whole world shows us two things, namely, one, that the overall culture of the Western world with its phenominal technological and industrial development, reveals inadequacies, notably in the sphere of spiritual and moral life, thus giving rise to undesirable condition of imbalance and unrest; two, that in the Eastern world, on the other hand, there also exists an absence of equilibrium in the sense that the prominent development in the spiritual and moral sphere is not even remotely matched by a parallel growth in the economic field, and that the East therefore yearns to share the enjoyment of the material welfare of the West.

Considering such state of affairs, it would seem to me that an equitable two-way traffic between East and West should be established, if mankind is to eventually arrive at an undivided world, a better world where peace, mutual appreciation and understanding and fruitful cooperation prevail. Now has the East, through the centuries, gone to great lengths in imbibing from the West. On the other hand, so far the West has shown little enthusiasm in making use of, or even acquainting itself with the untapped spiritual and moral resources with which the East is richly endowed, and through which the restoration of the badly needed balance and harmony in the life of the Western world may profitably be attempted. Such lukewarm attitude may be due to the intoxicating influence of its unprecedented industrial and technological advance.

In this connection, I think it is certainly a very good idea of Mr. Sunardjo Haditjaroko,M.A., to publish this well illustrated and absorbing little book. The Ramayana is indeed one of the most cherished stories from the Indonesian cultural store. Of the various types of shows based on the Ramayana — beside the immensely popular wayang-show — the 'sendratari Ramayana' deserves special mention. This is a glorious ballet involving not only 500 seasoned dancers in their magnificent costumes, but also a gigantic open-air stage with the serene Rara Jongrang temple as background. This impressive show can be watched on moonlit nights from June to October every year at Prambanan near Jogjakarta.

Therefore, I can warmly recommend this book to those who wish to familiarize themselves with at least part of the Indonesian culture, more particularly to the citizens of those countries which have a cultural agreement with Indonesia, and last but by no means least, to prospective tourists who wish to convince themselves of the truth of the famed words used by Multatuli when he referred to the Indonesian conglomeration of 13,000 ever-green and fertile islands and isles as "the girdle of jewels encircling the equator".

In conclusion I hope that this interesting book will succeed in reaching the goal for which it is written and may contribute toward the creation of a better understanding between East and West.

The Hague, 31st December, 1970   *Drs. M.Setiadi Kertohadikusumo,*
Cultural Attache

The main characters in this story.

Kingdom of Kosala
1. King Dasarata
2. Queen Kekayi
3. Rama (Crown Prince)
4. Sinta (Rama's wife)
5. Barata ⎱ Rama's brothers
6. Lesmana ⎰

Kingdom of Alengka
1. King Rawana or Dasamuka
2. Maricha ⎱ Rawana's brothers
3. Kumbakarna ⎰
4. Wibisana
5. Hindrajit (Crown Prince)
6. Trijata (Wibisana's daughter)
7. Wikateksi or Kataksini

Kingdom of Guakiskenda
1. King Sugriwa
2. Hanuman
3. Hangada
4. Hanila
5. Jembawan

Jathaju, king of birds

The Dalang

1. Preparing for the Show

The evening of the wayang performance has at last arrived. In the darkness the insects have already begun to fly around the unsteady flame of the oil lamp, which casts its dazzling light on the large white screen of the stage. At the lower part of the cloth-screen, the beautiful leather puppets are neatly arranged, their body-sticks firmly planted in banana-stems, placed beneath the screen itself. On the right hand side are the good characters, on the left hand side the bad. The open space between them, about two yards wide, represents the stage. Here the puppets will come to life and, like real human beings, will each in his own way pursue the endless path to human happiness.

The musical instruments, about fifteen in all, are in front of the screen.

It is now 8.30 p.m. One by one the musicians take up their positions. The leader of the group, the drummer, gives a few trial beats with his fingers. Other members of the team follow his example. A soft mixture of different sounds fills the room. But soon the noise suddenly stops.

More and more onlookers are flocking to the show. Some come from faroff places, eager to watch the wayang. As it is a shadow-play, the best place to watch from is of course on the dark side of the screen, reserved for women and girls. Men and boys watch from their seats on the same side of the screen as the lamp. It is true, they watch a shadow-play without seeing any shadows, but to see the beautiful puppets, to follow their movements, and to watch the handling of the instruments adequately makes up for the loss.

1

A five minutes to nine the Dalang joins the group. He takes up his position in front of the screen, right under the lamp, with the musicians behind him. Like everybody else, he is seated cross-legged. He then starts to burn incense in an open baked-clay oven ('anglo') in order to invoke the favour of the soul of his ancestors, the spirits and the higher Being: that he may be given the necessary endurance, clarity of thought, nimbleness of mind, and above all, glibness of tongue, because failure to accurately produce the different male and female voices of the characters — including individual mannerisms — failure to imitate closely the sounds of birds and beasts of the forest will to some extent lower his prestige.

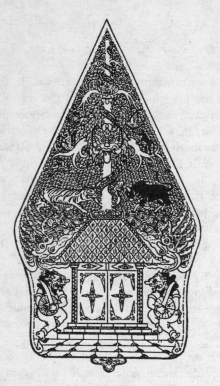

Gunungan

Next, he made sure that the sacrifical offerings for warding of interference from evil spirits are there: a live young cook, flowers and a cooked rice-cone with accompanying spiced meats.

Finally he alters the position of his right foot in such a way that the toes just touch the 'kechrek' or 'kepyak'. This is a device composed of a few metal plates, which hangs down from the edge of a wooden box ('kotak') on his left. By beating against the device with

2

a small wooden rod (called 'chempala') which he clutches between the first two toes of his right foot, the Dalang can — whenever he wishes — produce sharp or clipped sounds by which the movements or actions of the puppets can be emphasized, or, he can imitate the noise of the storm or thunder or the clangour of clashing weapons in a fierce battle.

He makes sure that everything is in its proper place: the 'chempala'; those puppets he will presently be needing, and finally, the all-purpose 'gunungan' (may be used to represent either the abode of the gods, or the forest, or a mountain or some huge obstacle) which is there in the middle of the stage. He has a quick look at the lamp. No, the flame is not large enough. So with a pair of pincers he gives a little pull at the wick. Now the screen lights up more brightly. The woman singer is there, the musicians are ready. The performance is about to begin.

2. The Dalang

Not everyone can be a Dalang. A Dalang is a most extraordinary man. First of all, he is a public entertainer. To amuse a great number of people is not an easy matter. He must be physically strong and healthy. Otherwise he would not be able to stand the strain. Just imagine, he is seated crosslegged for nine successive hours. He cannot have even a wink of sleep. He cannot get up from his seat until six o clook the next morning. He also has to strike the kechrek (rattle) with his right foot almost incessantly. He handles the puppets with both hands, imitates their different voices, tells jokes at the right times, and even sings every now and then. In addition, he controls the musicians without anyone among the audience ever noticing it. At intervals, he adjusts the wick of the lamp to prevent it from fading out. He does not leave it at that: he also has to keep the story fresh in his mind with every part of it in its right order.

Small wonder that people like him, admire him, and respect him at the same time. He has so many things to offer. He is a source of enjoyment, humour and recreation. He provides food for our eyes, ears, heart and mind. The deep enjoyment he gives us is unsurpassed by anything else. A good film gives us pleasure also, it is true, but it is usually forgotten as soon as it is over. But what the Dalang gives us usually stays much longer in our mind.

As far as money is concerned, he is satisfied with a relatively small sum. It in no way compares with what even the poorest film-actor in America gets for only one hour's acting. Foremost in the Dalang's mind is to serve the community. His greatest reward lies in the gratefulness of his audience, rather than in the amount of money he gets in return for his exacting work. Therefore, so far not one Dalang has been known to become really wealthy. No matter how much money he gets — as a popular performer he does receive a lot of money — he remains decently poor and humble. A Dalang behind the steering wheel of a sparkling Mercedes Benz would be a miracle. It would be equally fantastic for the famed filmstar Richard Burton to sit cross-legged for nine hours. He would probably die of cramp after three hours.

3. The Show Begins

If you are a Dalang, you need not read this, you know it already.

The time is now nine o'clock. The evening wind brings coolness and everyone is set for the wayang-show. The Dalang lifts the chempala (rod) with his left hand and — simultaneously with the soulful and haunting sound of the 'rebab' (two-stringed violin) he then gives a firm rap on the soundbox. Now everyone is all ears for what the allround entertainer has to tell. He quickly glances up at the lamp above his head, and after removing the 'gunungan' (mountain) from the centre of the stage, he then begins. . . . . . "There was once a vast country, called Kosala, which was known far and wide as a great glorious land. Its soil was very rich; its plains were very fertile where anything would grow, and grow well. Nor was there any shortage of water. It is therefore no wonder that crops always gave good harvests. Food and clothes were inexpensive. Everyone was well dressed; everybody was well fed. In all Kosala there was not a single thief. In fact, the thought of theft never entered anybody's head. Cows, horses and other domestic animals were never tied up at night, but moved about freely at all times. Nor were there any stables to lock them up in. The climate was good all the year round. 'Gotong-royong' or mutual help was strong among its citizens. They were polite and kind to each other as well as to strangers. At whatever door a tired traveller might knock, he was sure of a warm invitation to supper and the offer of a comfortable lodging for the night.

Mighty rivers wound their way across the land. The scenery gained added beauty from the lofty mountains, some of which were so high that their tops were forever hidden behind the clouds.

This happy and prosperous country was now governed by a noble king who always put his subjects' interests before his own. His name, Dasarata, was famous throughout the earth. How his subjects loved and admired him!

His palace was the largest and the most beautiful in the world. It was made of the most precious timber, marble and gold. In the extensive grounds and parks surrounding it grew the most wonderful plants and shrubs and flowers, and countless trees where birds of bright and various plumage had their nests. Fish of every kind and colour flashed and gleamed through the crystal-pure waters of its many lakes and pools and lily-ponds. In short, everything in the king's palace was a delight to ear and eyes. Kosala was indeed a great and glorious country.

4. King Dasarata Gives up the Throne

Now Dasarata had four children, all sons. In order of age, they were Rama, Barata, Lesmana and Satrugna. Brought up in wisdom and loving care, these four princes were always in perfect harmony with one another. They played, hunted and took exercise together. There were no handsomer young men in all Kosala. And how people loved them! In popularity they were second only to their father. Constant practice had made them expert in the use of bow and arrow, spear and sword. They were excellent horseriders. Their courage was unmatched. At regular times, they hunted tigers in the dense forests. No sooner was a beast in sight, then four flashing arrows swiftly pierced the weakest parts of its smooth-coated body.

In the art of climbing trees, they were second only to monkeys. At swimming too they were almost unequalled. No wonder the old King was proud of his offspring, in whom he found a never-failing source of happiness.

Though Dasarata was in his nineties, he desired to reign as long as he lived. However, the spirit was strong, but the flesh was weak. Very often Dasarata felt tired and fatigued. His eyesight and hearing became weaker every day. So in the end he decided to retire. According to the custom of the country the crown would pass to his eldest son, so that Rama was his legal heir and successor.

Now a coronation would be an event that could scarcely pass unnoticed, for the crowning of a new king invariably marked an important epoch in the life and culture of the people. So the aged King gave orders for Ayodya, the capital of Kosala, to be beautifully decorated and otherwise made ready for the glorious event. There was no one in the city who did not look forward to the magnificent ceremony. Everyone wanted to take part in the festival. Nothing was forgotten: buildings, towers, lamp posts, bridges and public carriages were made to look attractive. For days on end, people were talking about nothing else but the great event which was soon to take place. How they would love to see handsome Rama and his beautiful wife Sinta made King and Queen. They were certain that under Rama the glory and prosperity of Kosala would reach new heights.

But alas, the sun of their happiness was destined to be hidden by black clouds of sorrow, as we shall soon see.

5. A Dark Cloud on the Horizon

Everybody was looking forward to the great day — everyone, that is, except Queen Kekayi, the mother of Prince Barata. She had no personal grudge against Rama, yet it has always been her most cherished wish to see her son ascend the throne of the glorious and mighty realm of Kosala. For years, she had been seeking ways and means to make that dream come true. Custom and age old tradition gave precedence to the King's first-born son, and Kekayi had a great respect for tradition; yet she could hardly bear the thought that anyone but Barata would become king, even though Barata was not first in line of succession.

On hearing of King Dasarata's intention to abdicate the throne, she began to rack her brains in an effort to accomplish her life's ambition; but in vain. Tortured by anxiety, she had spent the past few days in a fever of restless excitement, and at night she had scarcely slept at all. She had even started neglecting her meals. How very unsettled and unhappy she felt!

But now it was that Mantara approached, Mantara, her faithful maidservant. A sly, evil little hag was this Mantara, always ready to undertake whatever task might please her mistress, even if it meant committing some dreadful crime. Observing the dark lines of sorrow around the Queen's eyes, she had done her best to console her. Soon, however, a brilliant idea flashed through her mind, and her own shrewd eyes glittered and glowed like burning coals with cunning satisfaction. She hastened to the Queen's room, to find Kekayi weeping bitterly. Seeing Mantara kneeling by her throne, Kekayi exclaimed, through her tears, "You know, Mantara, who it is for

10

whom all these preparations are being made. Would that they were in honour of my son Barata! But alas, that can never be, for the King has spoken, and Prince Rama has already been proclaimed his successor. I wish that I were dead!"

At this Mantara quickly answered, "Do not despair, my beloved Queen. His Majesty loves Prince Barata, too, and your heart's desire may yet be fulfilled."

"Foolish woman! Do you really believe that his Majesty will change his mind, now that his decision has been announced to the people?" asked Kekayi in a faint voice.

"Why not?" replied Mantara. "I have seen stranger things than that happen in my lifetime. Does your Majesty not recall how years ago she saved the King's life on the battle-field? Your Majesty will no doubt remember, too, the King's reward, which hitherto your Majesty has never claimed?"

At these words, the Queens face lit up. Ah, how true it was! How could she possibly have forgotten all about it? The King had indeed promised to grant her any two favours that she might ask of him; and of that royal indulgence, inspired as it had been by heartfelt gratitude, she had never so far wished to avail herself.

6. Kekayi Claims the King's Reward

The Queen lost no time in hastening to the King's chamber. It was unusual that she should trouble the old King in the middle of the night as she did on this occasion. But she had an excuse. Time was running short, for it was on the next day that Rama would be crowned. The King himself was not yet asleep. Kekayi knelt down beside him and attacked him with women's most powerful weapon: tears.

When the King asked her what was the matter, she replied, in a tone that would have melted any man's heart, "Your Majesty, forgive me. I am the most ungrateful creature on earth, for I am about to bring sorrow upon you." And when the feeble old King looked puzzled and at length encouraged her to speak, she said to him what she had already been repeating in her mind a hundred times before, "Do you remember the time — years ago — when I healed your wounds on the battle-field?"

"I certainly do, my Kekayi. I also remember that as a reward I promised to carry out any two requests that you wished to make. I take it that now you have come to claim your reward?" said the King without any sign of suspicion.

Then Kekayi continued, "Yes, Majesty. That is exactly the reason that I have come. But before I express my desire, promise first of all to fulfil whatever request I decide to make."

"That I promise, by the bones of my ancestors," said the weary old King, suppressing a yawn with difficulty. "State your wishes, and as true as I am king of glorious Kosala, I shall grant them immediately. Now, what are they?"

Then Kekayi started weeping again. When pressed by the King, she managed to say with down-cast eyes, "These are my two requests. First let Barata be crowned tomorrow. Second, let Rama be banished for fourteen years to the forest of Dandaka."

For a few moments the King was unable to utter a word. His breathing became difficult. His chest shook with sorrow, then he groaned as if a red-hot needle had been thrust into his feeble body. But at last he collected himself. His face flushed with anger. He trembled all over with rage. "What . . . what on earth did you say, you cruel, selfish woman? What wrong has Rama ever done to you? I would rather stop seeing the rays of the sun than grant your disgraceful requests."

But Kekayi persisted. Said she, "Do as you wish, your Majesty. Only I want to remind you that it is the King's duty to be true to his word. Break your promise, if you wish, but just remember that your subjects will lose their respect for you. You will go down in history as a king who cannot keep his promise."

7. Rama's Banishment

Kekayi's words fell upon the King's ear with the numbing force of hammer blows. Had he not sworn, but a few moments earlier, to grant her two requests, whatever they might be? And now, through no fault of his own, he had unsuspectingly walked straight into the trap she had so skilfully laid for him. The position in which he found himself was thus hopeless. It was that of a man caught between two fires. Two possibilities alone lay open to him: either to inflict upon Prince Rama, whose only crime was that of being his eldest son, a harsh and bitter exile, or to forswear his solemn oath and so earn himself the evil name of perjurer. After reflecting for some moments upon this agonizing dilemma, he at last reluctantly resolved to do as Kekayi wished, though his heart still bled within him.

Kekayi however was delighted. No human being had been known to survive long in the forest of Dandaka. Long before the fourteen years of his banishment were over, Rama would have found certain death. Then Kekayi's son Barata could reign over Kosala in peace.

On the day appointed for the coronation, the old King issued an announcement which, coming as a complete surprise to the citizens of Ayodya, left them shocked and stunned. For Prince Rama it was like a bolt from the blue. At first he was dumbfounded, but, plucking up courage, he approached his father and asked him for some explanation. It was then he learnt that his misfortune was of Queen Kekayi's making. The King declared that the promise he had so rashly made to Kekayi left him no choice but to yield to her demands, for the solemn pledge of a King must be inviolable. In consequence, he would have to command Prince Rama to leave the palace at once.

14

Sinta   *Rama*

As Rama was sadly taking his departure, there occurred an event as touching as it was unexpected. Prince Barata rushed out after his brother, seized him by the hand, and emphatically asserted that he would never deprive him of his rightful inheritance. With tears in his eyes, he urged him to remain. But, for Rama, the King's command was law, to which he felt himself bound, both as a loving son and as a loyal subject, in absolute obedience; and, in a voice choking with emotion, he replied, "No, no, my good brother. The crown belongs to you. Of that there can be no question. Therefore govern our great country in peace, with wisdom, mercy and justice, and you shall have my blessing. As for me, I must make my way to the forest of Dandaka, whence I shall not return before my fourteen years of exile are accomplished. And now may God be with you." With that he left Barata sobbing and strode on toward the great gate. But behold! What sight was that? All of a sudden, an enchantingly lovely woman came hastening after him, the people thronging close about her. It was none other than Sinta, Rama's beautiful wife, who now tenderly embraced him, and with heart-rending tears, begged to be allowed to share his exile.

8. *Dasarata Dies of Grief*

For a few minutes Rama let Sinta shed her tears freely. Then, as her sobbing decreased, Rama said, "No, my Sinta. You stay in the palace and await my return. You have no idea of Dandaka. It is crowded with devils and wild beasts. Your company would only increase my burden." But Sinta had no ears for these words. Instead, she held on to both his arms, quite determined not to let him go.

At this point Lesmana joined them. "I too," said he, "will accompany you and share your banishment, my dear brother. My life would be empty without you. So please let me come with you." Despite Rama's firm refusal, Sinta and Lesmana persisted. Finally Rama gave in. Then he turned to take leave of his father. "Goodbye, my father. Do not grieve too much, because I am sure the gods have willed it. I do not blame you, and I do not blame Queen Kekayi either. So let me part in peace." With that, Rama made for the exit, with Sinta and Lesmana close at his heels.

No words can describe the storm that raged in the King's heart. Unable to stand the strain, he soon fell ill and died. The banishment of Rama, followed too soon by the King's death, was a cruel blow to Kosala. Everyone went into mourning. Kekayi, too, mourned, but it was mere pretence, Inwardly she was glad that at last her wildest dreams would soon come true. But she did not know what the gods had in store for her. To her dismay, Barata flatly refused to listen to her. He pointed out to his mother that the crown belonged to Rama. "I shall see to it," said he, "that Rama is brought back to the palace to be proclaimed the new king. To act otherwise would be unworthy of me, and I do not want to reap the wrath of the gods."

But however much Kekayi begged, urged and wheedled, Barata did not budge an inch. The Queen became furious. She had gone too far; she had caused the King's death; she had wronged Rama. Even the flight of Sinta and Lesmana was indirectly her fault. And now, the crown which she had been fighting for by hook or by crook, was slipping through her fingers.

She had made her plans carefully, but had overlooked one thing: she had completely forgotten to consult Barata in advance. Had she done so, much unnecessary suffering could have been avoided.

9. Barata's Noble Attitude

As soon as the funeral rites were completed, Barata hastened off into the forest in search of Rama and his companions. At length he caught up with them and was able to break the sad news of the King's death, which they all felt to be a grievous loss. Barata insisted that, now that the wise old King was gone from them, the way was clear for Rama to assume control of their country's affairs. Rama was touched by this noble gesture of his brother's, but could not share the opinion which had inspired it. He countered with the argument that the death of their father merely strengthened their obligation to respect his wishes. He was therefore resolved to resign himself to the fate which had befallen him. Barata then proposed that, since Rama was unwilling to come back with him at once, he should govern Kosala as his deputy pending his eventual return. Bidding his kinsmen a final godspeed, Barata headed back towards Ayodya, while Rama and his faithful followers moved away deeper into the forest.

Barata's temporary regency was marked by prosperity and peace. He steadfastly rejected his mother's importunate and oft-repeated advice that he should have himself ceremonially crowned. Far from attempting to usurp Rama's prerogative, he caused the sword of state to be placed upon the empty throne in token of his brother's continued authority. This was a severe blow to Kekayi's ambition, but she did not give up hope. Rama would soon perish in Dandaka, and then her sweet dream would at last come true.

Meanwhile the trio threaded their way through the forest until they reached Dandaka. Now life in the forest was by no means easy, especially for those accustomed to the comforts and amenities of the city. For food they had to rely chiefly upon what they could discover amid the dense, lush vegetation that surrounded them on al sides; but it was not long before they had learned to distinguish poisonous herbs and plants from those that yielded them a rich supply of edible roots or shoots or nuts or fruit or berries, and soon they had also found places where they could gather up the eggs of ducks and other wild-fowl. When drinking water was not to hand, they were able to quench their thirst by sucking and chewing a particular species of thick, juicy grass. On the whole, they were succeeding in gradually adapting themselves to their jungle environment. Their worst enemy appeared to be fatigue. All three suffered to some extent from the stresses and privations of their new mode of living, and Sinta, perhaps, most of all, there were times when it seemed to her that her weary little feet, aching and throbbing with every step she took, would carry her no farther. Ah, how she missed her soft satin shoes! Often she felt as if she were walking upon rusty knives and long, sharp-pointed needles, and although she never once complained, it could not escape her companion's notice that she was sorely in need of rest and repose.

10. Rama Builds a Forest Home for Sinta

Rama was all too keenly aware of what Sinta must be suffering, so he decided to look round for a place in which they could settle comfortably for the remainder of their exile. They found a pleasant open space in the forest, where good drinking water was supplied by a small stream, and where was an abundance of fruits and vegetables. Finally they agreed to settle there and build a hut to protect themselves from the rain, wind and wild beasts. They cut down bamboo for the columns and walls; they used palm-leaves for the roof. To keep snakes out, they built the floor some distance from the ground. Situated under a tall, leafy tree, their little home was well protected from sun and rain.

The days passed quietly and calmly in this new dwelling-place, to which Rama gave the name of Panchawati. Sinta herself was never left alone in the hut, for they never felt entirely free from the threat of danger, which seemed to hover over them like the wings of a mighty eagle. When food was needed, only one of them went to fetch it; the other kept Sinta company.

One bright morning, when Lesmana was away in search of food for the little family, it would occur to Rama that he should make special arrangements in onder to keep Sinta out of harm's way. Said he, "Listen, Sinta dear, I want you to realize the possible dangers that may come to us at any time while we stay in this jungle. Therefore I am going to establish a mighty wall, an invisible one, that is, around our home. I tell you, under no circumstances shall you leave it." At these words Rama drew his holy kris out of its sheath, and, after planting its pointed end inch-deep into the ground, he then started to draw a large circle around the hut. Said Rama again, "As long as you remain inside this magic circle, no harm will ever be done to you!" Sinta took in every word of what Rama had said, and with bated breath she solemnly promised never to go beyond it.

Though life in the forest was not quite unbearable, Sinta often missed the court-ladies who had previously waited on her in the palace. There were often moments when she could hardly manage to hold back her tears. To cheer her up, Rama gave her a rabbit and a wild duck. Whenever he could, he brought her the prettiest flowers he was able to collect. On one occasion, Lesmana brought her a young monkey which he had found neglected by its parents; on another, Rama came across peacock chickens which he had found almost starving. The mother pea-hen had doubtless been killed by some wild beasts. In any case, when they saw Rama, they did not show any fear, but quite happily followed him to his hut. In the course of time the collection of birds and beasts grew into a kind of a small zoo. The task of caring for the new members of the family was entrusted mainly to Sinta, for whom it provided a most absorbing occupation, for the work was interesting in itself, and the little creatures in her charge gave her endless leisure and amusement. For the men, too, there were ample opportunities to keep fit and healthy — game to hunt, hills to climb, and streams to wade through.

Sometimes they even brought home with them honey of wild bees, while fruits in abundance was to be just for the picking. To all appearances then, life in Dandaka had turned out not so harsh as might have been expected.

But alas! How little they suspected the dangers which lay just below the surface of their peaceful existence.

11. Rawana Discovered their Hiding Place

Day followed day in peaceful succession, and month followed month. They hardly realized that thirteen years had already passed. Each new day was bringing them closer to civilazation, back to the happiness that they had long ago forsaken. From now on their minds were filled with plans. How they looked forward to the day when they could leave the forest and live comfortably in the palace once more. But alas! The days of their sufferings had not yet come to an end.

They were unaware that for quite some time now, they had been observed. Their presence in the forest had been discovered by giants who were the subjects of the much dreaded king Rawana, known also as Dasamuka. With his ten frightful faces he was like a bad durian: rough without and rotten within. His bloodshot eyes, his broad, flat nose, his bushy eyebrows, hairy chest and many mouths which resembled caverns, created the impression of a monster from a cruel nightmare. Besides, there were the yellowish teeth, some of which were so long that they almost reached to the cheek-bones. His character was altogether despicable. He was dishonest, cruel and uncommonly greedy. He felt it his right to destroy anything and everything that came his way. He delighted in wicked deeds. The screams of anguish from his victims were music to his ears. In short, Rawana was a completely inhuman, soulless and vicious barbarian.

When the giants reported to Rawana that Panchawati was inhabited, he started licking his dirty lips with delight. And what inhabitants they were! Two of them, he was told, were handsome men, and the third was a woman who was as beautiful as she was graceful. Rawana of course claimed Panchawati as his own. So he decided to go

22

Rawana

and see the trespassers with his own eyes, because he trusted no one. Now they would suffer at his hands, he thought, and how much enjoyment he would get out of it! Rawana then took to the air and it was not long before he was circling above Panchawati.

12. Caught Napping

Rama and his companions, who were having an afternoon nap away from the sweltering heat, failed to sense that danger was close at hand. How great was Rawana's delight when he finally spotted them from above the dense foliage. He flew close to the ground in order to have a good look at his prey. One glance at Sinta convinced him that she was the most wonderful woman he had ever set eyes on. To kill or not to kill the men, that was the first question in his head. As Rawana was considering what to do, a wasp alighted on Rama's nose. It woke him up, and soon his companions were awake too. Rawana cleverly slipped behind a big tree and quickly departed. As he could not make up his mind himself, he wanted to hear his brother's advice. Maricha, that was the brother's name, lacked the dramatic appearance of Rawana, but he was just and honest. Unlike Rawana, he spent his life in meditation and prayer. This was the wise man whom Rawana wanted to consult.

"Hallo, brother Maricha. How is life treating you? Are you still wasting your time as usual, always on your knees praying to God? I have come to you for advice. I wonder if you know about the trespassers on my hunting grounds. There are three of them, two men and one woman. What if I finish off the men and carry off the woman to my palace?"

Maricha listened in silence to his brother's silly chatter. At last he said in a grave voice, "Why can you not stop your evil practices? What harm have these people done to you? I discovered them long before you did. One of the men, called Rama, is the incarnation of the God Wisnu. Take my word for it. If ever you try to molest them, it may well be the beginning of the end of Alengka."

At this Rawana laughed with contempt. "I know you have always been a miserable coward. I have come to you for advice, but you try to scare me . . ."

Here Maricha interrupted, "Talk as much as you like, so long as you don't involve me in your low dealings. But remember, you are bringing ruin to all of us."

Rawana ignored these stinging words, because he needed his brother. Without Maricha's help, it would be almost impossible to steal the woman. They kept on arguing. Finally Rawana rose in violent anger. He drew his long glistening dagger and rushed forward. Knowing that Rawana was not joking, Maricha held up his arms. "Stop, Rawana! I give in. Since you are my bother, all right, I shall do whatever you wish."

Then the two plotted together until the srigunting started his early morning song from the treetops. At last, their plan was ready.

13. The Golden Deer

In the meantime Rama, Sinta and Lesmana were having a lot of fun with their pets. When feeding time arrived, it was a delight to see how the birds and animals took their food, each in its own special way. Their tame squirrel was a particular source of amusement for them. This little creature showed not the slightest fear of its masters. At one moment it would be sitting on Rama's knee, the next, it would run up his arm, sit on his shoulder and start polishing its shiny coat with its tiny tongue.

Suddenly Sinta's attention was attracted by the most wonderful animal she had ever seen. It was a beautiful little deer with a coat which shone like gold. The more Sinta watched it, the more charmed she became. "Look at that, Rama,"Sinta exclaimed excitedly, "Isn't it a little darling? I would give anything to have her. How wonderful she would look in Ayodya's royal gardens! Oh, please do catch her for me, Rama dear."

Rama replied, "Don't worry, you'll have her." With that, he leapt forward, but the animal, seeing him, playfully avoided his grip. To everyone's astonishment, she showed no apparent sign of fear. On the contrary, she started frisking and frolicking in front of them, just out of reach. Again Rama tried to catch her, but no! She sprang back, stood on her hind-legs and started to dance gracefully. Tears appeared in Sinta's eyes at such a display of elegance. Then suddenly, with the swiftness of an arrow, the deer made a jump away from those watching her. Rama felt that his honour was at stake. "Lesmana," he called out, "Look after Sinta while I'm away. I won't be long, but whatever happens, don't leave her alone." Even as he uttered these last words, he had set off in pursuit of the fleeing animal.

"I promise," answered Lesmana, "but take good care of yourself!" And this he shouted to make sure that Rama heard him.

14. Rama is Lured Away

So Sinta and her brother-in-law were left alone waiting for Rama to come back. They prayed to Sang Hyang Wenang, the Almighty, that Rama should be allowed to return safely to them with the prize. Minute followed minute and hour followed hour, but Rama did not come back. The deer seemed to have wings, so swiftly and lightly did it move along. Gradually Rama became suspicious and feared that he might be the victim of some clever trick. It had become evident to him that he was being deliberately separated from the others. Rama himself was getting weaker and weaker; his movement slower and heavier. "No," he said at last, "I shall never be able to catch her alive." Thereupon he took careful aim with his arrow. There was a sudden flash and the animal dropped to the ground. Rama dashed forward to seize his prey, but what strange sight was this that met his eyes? On the very spot where the deer had fallen, an elderly giant now lay writhing and twitching with pain. The arrow had torn a fatal wound just beneath the left shoulder. Yet even in the few moments of life that were left to him, he drew a last great deep breath into his lungs, and, summoning all his remaining strength, in a voice that sounded uncannily like Rama's own, gave out a long, urgent cry of distress: "Help! Help! He. .lp!"

Meanwhile, at some distance from the spot where Rama was now standing, Sinta and Lesmana were patiently awaiting his return. But as the shadows of the trees grew longer and Rama still failed to return, Sinta became apprehensive, and began to weep. "What can have happened to Rama? Surely he cannot have lost his way? He must be in danger. Maybe he is hurt, or perhaps, perhaps even . . ." Here her voice failed her, for she could not bring herself to utter the dreadful fear that was in her mind. But what was that? She pricked up her ears, for she thought she had heard Rama calling for help. "Lesmana, can't you hear something? Wasn't that Rama shouting for help? Do go to him, Lesmana. Run as fast as you can; otherwise you may be too late to save him."

Lesmana tried to soothe her, assuring her that the sound that had reached them could only have been the cry of some wild animal, reminding her how brave his brother was and of what powerful build, and adding that he had never been known to come off worse in any trial of strength and valour.

But Sinta, almost frantic with anxiety, would not heed his words. Again she urged him to make haste and go to his aid, but still he would not leave her. Finanlly, in desperation, she taunted him, "I know what the trouble is," she cried, "you . . . you want me, don't you?"

This accusation was more than Lesmana could endure. Her scathing words stung him into action, and he replied, "Look, Sinta, you know perfectly well that Rama made me promise not to leave you under any circumstances. If you yourself insist that I should break that promise, very well, I'll go. But take good care of yourself. See that the door is safely locked, and don't come out again on any account until Rama and I get back!"

So saying, he turned and sped away in the direction from which the call for help seemed to have come.

15. Sinta Kidnapped by Rawana

Sinta felt relieved that Lesmana had gone to the rescue. But what if he arrived too late? Lesmana himself might get into serious trouble. Oh, how she wished she had never been so foolish as to ask Rama to catch the deer. Now she could hardly forgive herself for such a childish whim. She trembled to think that both men might get killed. And what would become of her, a defenseless girl, alone and unarmed in the forest? And there she was, waiting behind locked doors, unable to do anything.

Then, all at once a blast of wind came to shake the hut. The sky which a moment before had looked clear and bright, quickly became dark and gray. At short intervals the lightning flashed; big drops of rain began to fall. And through the openings in the roof Sinta noticed how unnaturally bright the lightning was. There was something mysterious about it. Then, before she realized what was happening, somebody appeared outside the hut. It was an old man with a bent back, leaning on a rough wooden stick.

"Is anybody at home?" he enquired in a feeble voice. "Please allow me to shelter here until the rain stops."

Sinta was actually panic-stricken, but she pretended not to be afraid. She greeted the old man politely as every noble lady should. She remembered Lesmana's advice never to leave the hut. So she remained within, and invited the stranger to enter. In a flash, she realized her mistake, but too late! When she saw how the old man's eyes flashed and rolled so fearfully in his head, her lips lost colour and her blood ran cold. She could not help thinking of an old sheep with the eyes of a tiger. Stranger still, the weak voice changed into a

30

vigorous one when he said, "Madam, you may not know that this part of the forest is very dangerous. Now that you are here alone, you are in grave danger. Why do you stay here? Who are your companions and where are they?"

And when Sinta told him what had happened, the old man smiled broadly, displaying long, pointed teeth, most unusual in an old man. This gruesome sight made Sinta shudder. Sinta gathered her long, flowing hair about her, and prepared to make good her escape, but the old man stopped her, saying, "Don't run away. Come with me. I shall be able to help you."

Then something happened that almost made her swoon. The old man disapperared and in his place stood a towering giant with ten faces. "Don't be afraid, Sinta. Allow me to intruduce myself. You've been talking to Rawana, King of mighty Alengka. To be quite frank, I must confess that I've been wanting to meet you for some time, and now I've come here specially to escort you back to my palace."

Sinta, though almost beside herself with fright, managed to keep her voice steady as she replied, "I'm afraid I couldn't possibly go with you. Surely you must know that I am married to the heroic Prince Rama, who is destined one day to rule over the great realm of Kosala."

"But Rama is dead," retorted Rawana, with an evil leer on each of his ten faces. "My brother Maricha has just killed him. Didn't you hear his final screams? It's no use your waiting for him. You had much better come with me. I can make you the wealthiest queen in the world."

Sinta fell into a swoon. When presently she recovered consciousness, she found herself being carried through the air at a fantastic speed, and on glancing downward, she could just catch a glimpse of the familiar mountains, ravines, and forests of the land she had grown to love vanishing into the dim distance behind her.

16. Jathayu to the Rescue

Because of the terrifying rate at which Rawana was moving, the landscape quickly became blurred and indistinct. Obeying a sudden impulse, Sinta dropped her necklace, in the hope that someone might find it and give it to Rama.

With Sinta safely in his arms Rawana's happiness exceeded all earthly bounds. From now on, he believed his kingdom would be free of all misfortunes brought about by floods, pests or epidemics. He had come to believe that the prosperity and well-being of Alengka depended on the presence in his palace of the most beautiful woman in the world as his queen. The more Rawana thought about the many benefits which Sinta would bring to Alengka, the greater his happiness became. He was so absorbed in thought, that he had not noticed a dark spot higher in the sky which had been following him. It was Jathayu, king of birds, and a faithful friend of Dasarata, the news of whose death had not reached him. For some time this good bird had been cruising about the skies, when suddenly his attention was attracted by the sight of a woman with long, flying hair, being carried away by his sworn enemy Rawana. Jathayu descended a little. Then, to his horror and anger he discovered that the captive was none other than the beautiful Sinta, Dasarata's daughter-in-law. The problem which now faced him was how to help her. To attack Rawana in the air would expose Sinta to still greater danger. A fall from these heights would mean certain death to her. But if he should force Rawana to fight him on the land, he knew that the odds would be against him. As long as his body was touching the ground, Rawana would always survive, because of his talisman Panchasona. Finally

Jathayu made up his mind. There was no alternative but to grapple with Rawana in the air, if he wanted to rescue Sinta. Unfortunately, however, just at that moment Rawana chanced to look up. Knowing that his arch-enemy was above him, he held his dagger at the ready. When the large bird came closer, Sinta shouted at the top of her voice, "Help, good Jathayu!"

No sooner had Jathayu planted his sharp bill into Rawana's shoulder than the latter's dagger was firmly driven into the bird's chest. With a heart-rending shriek of anguish Jathayu fell through layers of air and finally struck the ground with a rescounding thud. The gaping wound in his body told him that death was near, but hoping that his life would last until someone could find him, he continued to struggle against death.

Jathayu

17. Rama in Despair

With Maricha killed, Rama started on his way back to Panchawati. It was now quite clear to him that he had been the victim of a trick, in allowing himself to get separated from his companions. He sincerely hoped that Lesmana had not left Sinta alone. But he was not quite sure that Lesmana had heard his last words, for he remembered that he, Rama, was running after the deer when he called out the last instruction to his brother. The only thing of which he was certain, was that he had not heard Lesmana's reply and so he hoped that if Lesmana had not heard him, then Sinta did, because she was a little closer to him at that time.

In his anxiety, Rama did not notice where he was going. With eyes cast down, he did not realize that his strong feet had already carried him a long way from the spot where he left Maricha. Suddenly he gave a start when the sound of quick footsteps came to his ears from the opposite direction. He immediately sensed that something was wrong. What a surprise when he saw that it was none other than Lesmana who approached him. Lesmana in his turn, felt only relief on recognizing his brother.

Rama cupped his hands and shouted, "Hallo! Where's Sinta? Quick, tell me where she is!" Rama could scarcely control himself now that it was clear to him that either his last words had not been heard, or that, if they had, Lesmana had failed to observe them. When the two brothers stood face to face, neither dared to speak. Their eyes met in a deadly stare and the ensuing silence proved more eloquent than words. Rama's reproachful eyes struck Lesmana like dagger-points. At last Lesmana broke the silence and explained to

Rama in a few words just exactly what had happened. The situation was now clear. Rama's worst fears had been realized.

Without a word Rama took to his heels and sped like lightning to Panchawati, with his brother in hot pursuit. On finding his little bamboo hut deserted, Rama was overcome with despair. Where on earth could Sinta be? No doubt the hostile giants had stolen her, but where could Rama look for her? Who was there to tell him? Perhaps at that very moment, she was in danger of losing her life. Immediate action was absolutely necessary, but where was Rama now to turn? Such were the thoughts that tormented the desperate husband, as he and Lesmana abandoned the little hut to go in search of their beloved Sinta.

18. On the Right Trail

Rama no longer blamed his brother. After all it was Sinta herself who had forced him to leave her unattended; and on learning that Sinta had been instructed to lock herself securely in and not to venture forth till their return, Rama grew more and more bewildered.

Then it so happened that they almost stumbled against a huge bird lying limply on the path. Rama lowered his ear to the bird's chest and discovered that life had not yet entirely fled from the motionless body. It seemed to be suffering terribly. Then, suddenly, Jathayu's body began to tremble. Feeling someone gently stroking his wing, the good bird opened his great blood-shot eyes and with a great effort he gasped that he had not succeeded in rescuing Sinta from the hands of the wicked Rawana. Thereupon Jathayu's body began to quiver rapidly, but after a few seconds it gradually sank into motionless silence. Jathayu was no more. Rama and Lesmana blessed Jathayu's soul, and prayed to the gods that he should be given a peaceful restingplace in heaven. With a last farewell to the noble bird, the two brothers turned and headed south, but as their way led through jungles and swamps, they did not succeed in moving very fast.

By noon of the seventh day they arrived at the foot of a high mountain. As their feet became sorer and sorer at every step, they decided to rest on one of its slopes. Rama did not know that mount Reksamuka — for such was the name of the mountain — was the stronghold of an army of wanaras, a race of huge but noble apes. Before long, the bothers' presence was discovered by guards of the outpost. Their commander, named Hanila, a bluish ape, approached them in a respectful manner. He asked them who they were and what they were doing in the wanaras' territory. In a sad tone Rama revealed to him that he was looking for his wife Sinta, who had been carried away by Rawana, the king of the giants. Then, to his delight, Rama learned from Hanila that a few days before, Rawana had been seen flying southward in great haste over mount Reksamuka. Not only that! To the astonished eyes of Rama, Hanila then produced something which Rama immediately recognized as Sinta's diamond necklace. His heart leapt with joy when, with trembling hands, he received it from Hanila. Now he knew that he was one step closer to his beloved wife and that he had at last found the right trail.

19. Rama Gained a Powerful Ally

In reply to Rama's questioning, Hanila declared himself to be a commander in the service of Sugriwa, King of the wanaras, and indeed the rightful ruler of the vast kingdom of Guakiskenda, from which, however, he had been driven out by one Subali. King Sugriwa had established his stronghold on Mount Reksamuka, where, for years now, he had been anxiously awaiting an opportunity to win back the throne that was legally his; but the task of recovering his heritage was by no means simple, for, through the veins of the usurper Subali, instead of ordinary red blood, there flowed a mysterious white fluid that rendered him quite invulnerable to normal weapons. If Rawa would agree to help Sugriwa in that venture, it was certain that Sugriwa would offer to requite the favour, on the principle that one good turn deserves another. To attack the mighty Rawana single-handed, continued Hanila, would be to court disaster, but even Rawana might possibly be overcome if Rama had at his disposal a whole army of fearless apes.

Rama's heart was gladdened by these tidings. He had been brought up in the belief that justice will always prevail, and that it is the duty of every human being to resist evil wherever and in whatever guise he may encounter it, and he was therefore very willing to aid Sugriwa in his struggle against a manifest injustice.

It was not long before an alliance was concluded whereby, in return for Rama's active support of his rightful claim to the throne of Guakiskenda, Sugriwa promised to assist him in his fight against Rawana.

In his eagerness to rescue Sinta as soon as possible from the clutches of that evil monster, Rama urged King Sugriwa to prepare for battle without delay. Not that Sugriwa needed any urging, for that was just what he himself wanted.

A few days later, followed by Rama and Lesmana, Sugriwa set off for Guakiskenda, to settle his account with Subali, Sugriwa was now confident that with Rama's help, he would this time overpower his opponent and would finally realize his fondest dreams.

20. Sugriwa Defeats Subali

Having reached the borders of Guakiskenda without incident, they rested there for a few hours to gather all their strength for the impending battle. Subali, promptly warned by his scouts of Sugriwa's arrival at the frontier, was meanwhile making his own preparations for the inevitable encounter.

When at last the rival kings came face to face, they halted in their tracks and glared at each other with expressions of fierce resentment. Then they started circling cautiously round each other, but drawing steadily closer, now erect, now crouching, now bent almost double, now even crawling forward on the ground. Every so often one or the other of them would bare his fangs and let out a blood-curdling hiss. But for some time neither would take the offensive, each waiting for the right moment to lunge forward and tear his adversary to shreds. This wary mutual stalking went on for nearly an hour, and still they had not come to grips, each fearing to lower his guard by dealing the first blow. At length, however, growing impatient, both leapt forward simultaneously and seized each other by the throat. For what seemed an age they groaned and grappled and wrestled, turning and twisting with the rapid fury of a whirlwind, and gripping each other so tightly that the air was filled with the sounds of harsh panting, straining muscles, and creaking bones.

For one instant, Sugriwa was able to lift his opponent clear of the ground, until Subali, wrenching himself free, grasped him round the neck and below the right knee, and raising him as high as he could, dashed him down with such violence that he was forced to his knees. Quick as lightning, Subali was on him again, punching and pummell-

Sugriwa

ing and choking him to insensibility. Finally he held Sugriwa, now
reduced to helplessness, by both ears, and paused to draw a long deep
breath, that he might relish to the full his great moment of triumph.
He was on the very point of biting off Sugriwa's head, when, suddenly, a dazzling streak of light flashed through the air and pierced
his pounding heart. That momentary pause for breath had been Subali's undoing, for it was Rama's magic arrow that had penetrated his
scaly flesh and that now sent wave upon wave of deadly poison
coursing quickly through his anguished veins. His huge head swam,
his glazed eyes rolled with pain, his great, ungainly body reeled and
tottered and collapsed in a convulsive heap upon the blood-stained

41

earth. Sugriwa slowly scrambled to his feet and knelt down before Rama in token of his gratitude. He knew that, but for Rama's timely intervention, he would surely have perished.

A touching scene now followed, as all the commanders in what had been Sugriwa's own army before the expulsion from Guakiskenda, came forward in a body to pay him homage and renew their oath of loyalty to his person and his standard. For too long had they been forced to endure the tyrannous regime of Subali.

The next day witnessed Sugriwa's coronation, followed by a royal banquet to which all his friends and senior officers were invited. Parties were held throughout the entire realm, and the whole country rejoiced with festive song and dancing at the restoration of their rightful and righteous king.

21. Hanuman Volunteers to Visit Alengka

Sugriwa nobly lived up to his promise. As soon as the merry noise of rejoicing had died away, he assembled his counsellors and commanders for a discussion with Rama. All were aware that the sending abroad of a large expeditionary force was a minor enterprise in comparison with the actual conquest of Alengka. First of all a careful plan had to be drawn up. For that purpose, it would be necessary to reconnoitre the enemy's territory, to ascertain the exact location and size of his defences, and, last but not least, to discover what kinds of weapons were in his possession. The first problem confronting them was that no one had ever been to Alengka — or at any rate no one who might have been there had ever returned alive — so that nobody knew exactly how to get there, though all had heard how dangerous it was to try.

First of all they had to decide what scouts to send to Alengka to spy out the land and to find out where Sinta was imprisoned. Now it so happened that two commanders volunteered at the same time· their names were Hanuman and Hangada. Both were equally brave in battle, both were equally eager to go, but only one was needed. As neither was willing to withdraw, a quarrel soon arose and from words they came to blows. After a short but vigorous struggle, however, Hangada was forced to acknowledge Hanuman's superiority. And so it was decided that Hanuman was the man to go.

He himself, though well aware of what dangers must lie in wait for any intruder, was yet prepared to brave them all, feeling as he did that what was at stake was nothing less than the welfare of mankind. So long as Rawana remained alive, the world would never enjoy

Hanuman

untroubled peace. Hanuman was accordingly determined to put an end to Rawana's evil practices, even if it should cost him his life.

The distance to Alengka was very great and Hanuman was unsure of the way. He did, however, know that it lay to the south, and so, fired with enthusiasm, he vowed never to return unless he could bring back some news of Sinta's whereabouts.

Rama then presented him with a diamond ring by which he could prove to Sinta that he was no imposter. Hanuman bade farewell to his comrades, and, with a stout heart, set out to face whatever perils might lie ahead of him.

44

22. Hanuman Encounters Wikateksi

About the approaches to Alengka Hanuman had no reliable information. All he knew for certain was that, some time before, Rawana was reported to have been sighted crossing the sky in a southerly direction. He therefore decided to take the risk of heading due south. To avoid obstacles at ground level, he availed himself of his magic powers and took to the air. Favoured by a strong northerly wind, his journey was at first a smooth one, but, towards evening on the third day, he reached a point where land gave way to the sea. Soon he could watch the foam-flecked surf beneath him, and could make out the towering breakers incessantly rolling and crashing against the coastal cliffs. For two more days he continued his southward flight, without seeing anything but the grim expanse of bluish water stretching away below him and reflecting the calm and cloudless sky above. There was nothing to indicate the lurking presence of danger.

Danger, however, there was, for Hanuman's progress had not passed unobserved. Submerged in the depths lay Wikateksi or Kataksini, Alengka's formidable ever-watchful guard, a creature of enormous dimensions, even for an ocean-going giant, whose mouth alone was so wide that he could easily have gulped down a full-grown whale, had such a morsel chanced to tempt him. His vast body remained concealed under water, leaving only his swivelling eyes and part of his head protruding slightly above the surface. He never slept.

For months and months Wikateksi had lain there on guard, and, so far, nothing had happened. But what was that? His suspicious nature had been thoroughly aroused by some white speck gliding high in the air. This unfamiliar object greatly puzzled him. Thrusting his head and shoulders right out of the water, he opened his cavernous mouth and started sucking in air with such force as to create a whirlwind, which swiftly grew in size and strength until before long Hanuman found himself caught in its inexorable grip, spinning helplessly round like a top, and being drawn down in a frenzied spiral, closer and closer to the surface of the sea. Hanuman was panic-stricken. The eddying turbulance of the gale was making him feel weak and giddy; its dreadful howling nearly deafened him. Then, after a sudden, stupendous blast, everything grew suddenly silent. To his great surprise, he discovered that he was no longer in the air; instead he found himself in a place which was extremely hot, humid and dark. "At last", he thought, "my final hour has come."

23. Hanuman Puts an End to Wikateksi's Life

However much Hanuman pushed and pulled and kicked, he could not escape from the darkness of his prison. Even more exasperating was his inability to discover in what kind of pit he lay immured. Was he caught in the stifling depths of some immense volcano or entombed in the vastness of some dark cavern?

Then Hanuman pulled something which felt like a slippery eel. There was a loud groan. He gave a second pull, but now much harder, and a still louder groan was heard. Hanuman now concluded that he had been swallowed by some huge monster. He ventured to ask in a loud voice who it was. Imagine his horror when he was told that he was caught in Wikateksi's stomach, and that he should prepare to die. Hanuman, however, asked to be released, explaining that he was on his way to Alengka to rescue Sinta. He was soon to learn that he had said too much, for Wikateksi, thus assured of his victim confined in the roomy hold of his stomach, promptly snapped his great jaws shut, and closed his blubbery lips, and began to submerge.

Hanuman shouted with all his might, but Wikateksi made no reply. There was no getting out of this terrible prison; so Hanuman resigned himself to his fate. Soon, however, an idea struck him. If he made use of his supernatural powers, he could expand his size. So he set to work . . . twice, four times . . . ten times. Suddenly there was a cracking noise; Wikateksi roared with pain. Hanuman went on swelling and swelling until at last his captor, in a torment of pain and fury, burst into a thousand pieces. Hanuman hastily scrambled clear of the wreckage, rejoicing to see the light of heaven once more.

His recent experience had been unpleasant, it was true. Nevertheless it had taught him a useful lesson. In future he would have to be very careful and avoid unnecessary risks.

He looked round at the scattered remnants of the giant's body, and finding a length of flotsam that would serve as a spring-board, he leapt up from it into the air and flew off at great speed. He felt strangely refreshed after his brief imprisonment, and hoped that he would be able to reach the Alengkan frontier without further incident.

24. Hanuman Arrives in Alengka

It was not long before Hanuman sighted land. Flying over it, he had time to admire its clear rivers winding their way through green and fertile meadows and red-skinned giants with long, unruly hair, as they laboured among the rising crops in the fileds. To his delight, he was soon able to distinguish the walls of a very large city looming up in the distance. "That must surely be the Alengkan capital," he thought. To avoid capture, he decided to wait outside the city walls until it grew quite dark. So as not to be recognized, he turned into an ordinary monkey, in the hope that he would thus be able to move about unnoticed.

When the evening star appeared in the sky, Hanuman left his hiding-place. He scaled the city walls without difficulty. There he lingered for a while to enjoy the enchanting view spread out before him; for what he now beheld was something utterly unexpected: broad stately avenues lined with shady trees, tall buildings of unfamiliar design, but curiously attractive, and colourful marble towers and cupolas picked out by brilliant illumination — such was the panorama that unrolled itself to his astonished gaze. Who would ever have thought that a city in the kingdom of giants could be so beautiful?

Hanuman could not help being proud of himself, now that he was safe and sound within the walls of Alengka's capital. But he was very anxious to discover the place where Sinta was hidden. He forgot his fatigue, because every minute might be precious to Sinta. A sense of power arose within him. He watched the people as they moved about the streets — mostly large, glum-looking creatures they were, with eyes that rolled peculiarly in their heads. He was glad to see a

49

great number of ordinary monkeys everywhere, for, he thought, they would form a safe screen for all his movements in the city. Now he would be able to go anywhere he wished, unnoticed by these sharp-eyed giants. He started calmly investigating every part of the city. He went from one building to another, poking his head round open doors, and peeping through lighted windows. Sometimes he climbed trees in order to get a better view. He even crept through windows without attracting anyone's attention. By about midnight he had discovered the king's chambers. Luck was with him, for there below him he saw Rawana, lying on a golden couch, half asleep. Hanuman was quite sure of his identity, for no one but him could have had ten faces.

25. Hanuman Makes Good Use of his Time

In the course of his explorations, Hanuman was lucky enough to discover the arsenal where all kinds of offensive and defensive weapons were stored. Soon afterwards, he came upon the women's quarters, which were quite distinct from all other parts of the palace. The walls were made of the most exquisite stones and marble. Beautiful carpets covered the floors and stairs. Look where he might, Hanuman could find no trace of Sinta, but he would not abandon his quest until the first strident crowing of the roosters startled him with the reminder that dawn was rapidly approaching. Streetsweepers were already starting on their rounds, cleaning and tidying the vast squares and the great echoing thoroughfares. And gradually the ancient city awoke from its slumbers and stirred to the fresh life and labour of a new day. Although, in his present form, he felt fairly safe, he had no wish to run any unnecessary risk of detection and thus spoil his chances of success; so he crept on all fours to a nearby tree and clambered up into its luxuriant foliage to hide and to snatch some hours of rest. During the day, he dit not need to leave his shelter to look for food, for he had only to stretch out his hand to be able to pick the fruit with which its branches were laden.

Hanuman must have slept for some hours, for he suddenly realized with a start that the sun was now high in the sky. Then he was pleasantly surprised to hear two women chatting in the shade of his tree. From the way they were dressed, he assumed that they were servants. He listened carefully. Suddenly his face lit up when the women mentioned the name of Sinta. Then, when one of them left, Hanuman quickly slipped down to a low branch, and whispered, "Please don't be frightened. I've come here in search of Sinta. There's been so much talk of her extraordinary beauty that I'm very eager to see for myself what she's really like. You shall have a handsome reward if you can tell me where I may be able to set eyes on her."

At first, the girl thought her imagination must be playing tricks on her. On looking round, she could see nothing but a small monkey perched on the bough just over her head. Not until the request had been repeated did she sufficiently recover from her surprise to answer, "The best time to see Princess Sinta would be in the evening. If you will wait here till then, I myself can show you the way."

Thus encouraged, Hanuman withdrew into the shelter of the upper branches to await the coming of night.

26. Hanuman's Great Moment

As dusk was falling, the young lady returned as she had promised, to guide Hanuman to Princess Sinta's apartments. There she left him, just as he had secretly hoped she would, to his own devices. Finding the Princess alone in her chambers, he quickly approached and whispered in her ear that he was Rama's messenger. At first she could hardly believe him, until the sight of her husband's ring, which she at once recognized, convinced her that he was speaking the truth. It was only by a great effort that she was able to restrain her delight, and her eyes shone with mingled joy and relief. Hanuman glanced carefully round to make sure that their conversation could not be observed or overheard before telling her that Rama was on his way to rescue her and would be there within the month. His message thus delivered, he took his departure with the request that she should mark her pavilion distinctively with young coconut leaves.

Wishing to gain a clearer notion of the enemy's strength, Hanuman decided to appear in public before his unsuspecting hosts. He resumed his normal shape, and from the very top of a high building that overlooked a broad and crowded street, he gave vent to a long ear-splitting howl. All eyes were suddenly directed upwards to the gigantic white ape, who now yelled down at the astonished crowds, "Mark what I have to say, you foolish people of Alengka! It is I, Hanuman, who am speaking to you, Hanuman, messenger of the far-famed Rama, whose wife your wicked king has so shamefully and cruelly abducted. I warn you that the time is close at hand when Rawana must pay the penalty for his sins. Long live Prince Rama!"

Hindrajit

Before the populace had fully grasped the import of his words, he uprooted a huge palm-tree, and, brandishing it like a massive club, he began to batter it against towers and other edifices. Fragments of tile and slate and stone and glass rained clanging down on to the streets. Shrieking and screaming, the panic-stricken crowds took to their heels, badly shaken at the sight and sound of their lofty buildings crumbling and tumbling about them in ruins.

When Rawana heard what was happening, he swore that he would roast the intruder alive, and ordered a company of soldiers to capture him, but Hanuman, still high above the streets, and as it seemed, well

54

out of harm's way, calmly went on with his work of destruction. In his enthusiasm, however, he failed to notice Hindrajit, the Crown-Prince of Alengka, who had hurried to the scene and at that very moment was taking careful aim with his powerful bow. The shot was a good one. Hanuman reeled as the shaft found its mark, and, losing his balance, plunged headlong down into the midst of a multitude of angry warriors, several of whom he killed in his fall.

27. The Attempt to Burn Hanuman Alive

A roar of triumph rose from the crowd as they rushed upon the ape, temporarily lamed and dazed by his fall, and fettered him with strong chains. After some manoeuvring, they loaded him on to a large wagon and brought him before Rawana, who, gnashing his teeth with vindictive rage, gave orders that their captive should be burnt at the stake over a slow fire!

Hanuman soon found himself surrounded by great heaps of wood in the centre of a wide square which had rapidly filled with a dense throng of spectators. His arms and legs were shackled with heavy chains and his ears were half deafened by the shouts of the frenzied mob that had come to witness and to gloat over his execution.

At this dark moment of his life his thoughts turned to Agni, god of fire, to whom he appealed for help. Immediately his prayer was granted, for a wall of scorching flame sprang up to separate him from the watching crowds, but at the same time the air was darkened by swirling columns of black smoke which made it increasingly difficult for him to breathe.

Suddenly, Hanuman bestirred himself, and, with a superhuman effort, contrived to burst his bonds and wrench himself free. Flinging the shattered chains into the midst of the merrymakers, and snatching up a glowing brand from the pile, he leapt out at them through the flames, swinging his improvised torch and scattering sparks as he went. The shouts of triumph at once gave way to shrieks of terror, Hanuman's lameness had now miraculously worn off, and another mighty leap carried him to the top of a nearby building, where, poised on the edge of the roof, and whirling the huge firebrand round him, he looked like some great white ghostly avenger from another world. As he made his way out of the panic-stricken city, he began to set fire to everything that lay in his path, though taking care not to damage the building marked with coconut leaves. A strong wind fanned the blaze, and before long a large part of the town was in flames.

Satisfied for the moment with the results of the raid, and having assured himself that Sinta's pavilion was safe, he shook the dust of the distressed capital from his feet, and set out on the return flight to Guakiskenda.

28. Hanuman Bridges the Strait

Hanuman was quite content with the outcome of his mission, for he now had a much clearer idea of how that old reprobate Rawana could be defeated. The first blow, he told himself, was half the battle, and he knew how destructive that first blow of his had been; but now, since he could imagine how ancious Rama must be to learn what had happened, he lost no further time in returning to Guakiskenda.

On hearing that Sinta was alive and well, Rama was moved to tears of relief and thankfulness, and he was even more delighted to discover that there was a good chance of his being able to release her from the clutches of the odious Rawana.

So greatful indeed, was Rama for all that Hanuman had done that he decided to adopt him as his own son and to confer upon him the name of Ramadayapati. Such an honour was more than Hanuman had ever expected and left him almost speechless with happiness.

Sugriwa was better than his word. Not only did he keep his promise to provide a powerful army, but, to Rama's immense gratification, he also offered to take part in the campaign himself. Moreover, as everyone who could bear arms was eager to join them, there were enough well-trained soldiers to make up seven army corps, under the command of Rama, Lesmana, Sugriwa, Hanuman, Hangada, Hanila and Jembawan.

The morale of the troops could scarcely have been better, for all were looking forward with keen anticipation to the battle that they hoped would be decisive. Here at long last was their opportunity to put an end to Rawana's career of crime. The wanaras had more than enough of his insensate cruelty; now, they felt, the tide was beginning to turn in their favour. Rama issued orders that no time should be wasted and that preparations should go forward both by day and by night.

At last came the date fixed for their departure. What a noble sight it was to see seven armies of seasoned troops, eager to engage the enemy, and conscious of the rightness of their cause, moving southward in close column with Hanuman marching at their head to guide them! Each army had its own colourful uniform, its own bold ensigns and bravely fluttering pennants, their bright weapons glittered and glinted in the fresh morning sunlight, and the earth shook with the rhythmic sound of their rapid, inexorable advance.

When they reached the coast, however, their steady march was brought to an abrupt halt, for there ahead of them the sea surged and boiled, in a fury of pounding surf through the strait that separated Alangka from the mainland. How were they to cross? To bridge that formidable chasm seemed quite out of the question, for, though the sound that lay between them and Alengka was by no means wide, the violence of its currents and the sharpness of its cruel, jagged rocks would spare neither man nor beast nor boat. For a moment, even Hanuman was at a loss. But then he recalled the saying

'By mutual confidence and mutual aid
Great deeds are done and great discoveries made!'

Here, then, was the solution! Was it not true that countless droplets of water combined to make a mighty ocean? And could not a host of fearless wanaras conquer this narrow arm of the sea? A road must be built across it, and without delay. He himself would set the pace.

At once he picked up a huge boulder and hurled it down into the raging waters. Following his example, the whole mighty host set to work with a will, and, as there were plenty of suitable materials strewn along the coast, their task proceeded without pause, everyone lending a hand.

Massive stones were sunk into the water. Tall, stout tree-trunks were driven into the sea-bed as piles, or lashed together with strong, flexible tendrils to serve as guiding-lines or as pontoons. Shale and shingle, rocks and boulders, were poured or plunged in an orderly pattern into the swelling surf, and, slowly but surely, from the hard materials that had lain to hand in the nearby woods and among the craggy cliffs, a mighty causeway began to emerge. Incessantly, without rest, they toiled for seven whole days and seven long nights, until at last their gigantic project was complete, and a viaduct rose sturdy and strong above the battering waves.

From the menace of nature, their willing cooperation had snatched a heroic victory. The strait had been conquered, and the way now lay clear for the seven armies to enter the mysterious kingdom of Alengka.

29. The Start of Rawana's Nightmare

Rawana had always believed the Strait of Alengka to be completely impassable. It is therefore easy to imagine what a shock it must have been for him when Hanuman, a white ape, first appeared in the capital. Never before had any outsider set foot uninvited in his realm. Any who might have attempted so hazardous an enterprise had perished either in the turbulent waters of the Strait or at the hands of his ever-watchful guards. Rawana was furious, embittered by a new awareness that his defences were not, after all, impregnable, that Hanuman's raid had marked a new epoch in Alengkan history, and that the era of splendid isolation which his kingdom had enjoyed for so many centuries might soon become a vague, dim memory of a vanished past. He had always felt himself perfectly entitled to throw his weight about among his neighbours, to bribe or bully or frighten or threaten them, but the idea that anyone else might want to do the same to him had never crossed his mind. He had always fancied that the world existed for his personal convenience and that other lived in it merely to serve him. From now on this fondly cherished illusion would be hard to retain. No longer could he exert his despotic authority unopposed. Never again would he enjoy a good night's sleep, serenely undisturbed by haunting shapes of fear and envy and revenge. Now that one intruder had been able to enter and to leave Alengka with impunity, and even to reduce whole districts of his capital to smouldering ruins, what would become of Alengka if a whole army of such creatures were to invade his shores? — for he was shrewd enough to guess that Hanuman's raid was meant only to pave the way for a full-scale invasion. What if this spy had ferreted out the most closely guarded secrets of his inner defences?

Rawana had been tormenting himself for some time with these disquieting thoughts when a messenger was shown in. Dripping with sweat, and panting like a frog in agony, he was barely able to gasp out the news that the country had just been invaded by a great force of foreign troops, who were now encamped in the coastal forests. Rawana gave vent to his feelings in a loud obscenity. His worst fears, it seemed, had now become a grim reality.

Quickly, he sent for all his senior officers, and, after reproaching them for letting Rama carry the war into their own homeland, he gave brisk orders for immediate action: first, the chief divisions were to be alerted without a moment's delay; secondly, half of them were to be stationed within the city walls, while the other half were to counter attack the invaders; and thirdly, the guard on Sinta's pavilion was to be doubled forthwith.

Some of the generals looked angry and stared resentfully at the floor; they had long disapproved of Rawana's evil rule, but none had

Wibisana

had the courage to challenge him openly. Today, however, they felt that it was high time for someone to take the first step and tell the king in plain terms what they thought of him. Their elected spokesman was Wibisana, the king's own brother, who now came forward and tactfully pointed out that it was Rawana himself who, by his abduction of Sinta, had provoked Rama into invading Alengka. If Rawana were willing to let Sinta go, a great deal of bloodshed, with much loss of life and property, might even now be averted.

62

Scarcely had Wibisana finished speaking when Rawana leapt forward, and, in the presence of all the assembled commanders, struck him full in the face. This unforgivable insult led to a bitter quarrel and ultimately to Wibisana's decision to desert Rawana and join the invaders.

30. The First Clash

It was just on midnight when the defenders came streaming out from the city gates, intending to challenge the enemy to a pitched battle on open ground. The Alengkan infantry marched steadily forward, encountering not so much as a reconnaissance patrol, until they reached the fringes of the forest. But, to their astonishment, the forest seemed deserted; all was quiet; not a leaf stirred. For some minutes they continued their advance. Not a single ape was to be seen. Where on earth could the invaders be? Perhaps it was all a mistake?

Then, all of a sudden, there was an eerie screech. The apes had been there all the time, lying in ambush for the clumsy giants. Hearing the signal — for such it was — they swung nimbly down from the branches, and, falling upon the giants with a battle-cry that struck terror into the hearts of their opponents, they clung to their heavy limbs, climbed up on their shoulders, and began to bite off their ears and noses. Howls of pain rent the midnight air. Never had the tranquil forest of Alengka known such a cacophony of moans and grunts and screams. Unaccustomed to this style of warfare, the giants were taken completely by surprise. Just as one of them was on the point of dealing his assailant an annihilating blow, another ape would bite him viciously in the calf of his leg or the softest part of the back and send him sprawling. A few more well aimed bites and scratches, and the apes would be back among the trees, well beyond the reach of the perplexed and frustrated Alengkans, and already gathering themselves for their next cunningly directed attack.

Nothing could have been more demoralizing than these sporadic assaults, which invariably came when least expected and from the most unexpected quarter. The giants had never before experienced such harassing tactics, nor had their training prepared them in any way for an enemy so lightning swift and so elusive. Weary and worn, battered and bleeding, when daylight dawned they were wholly at the mercy of the apes. Hundreds had sought refuge in flight; thousands lay dead or helpless on the field of battle. Many were too badly mauled to be able to walk, but all who could rallied together and beat a disorderly retreat, hotly pursued by the wanaras, as far as the city walls. Only there did the invaders pause for breath, and withdrew to shelter in order to rest and to regain their strength.

As Rawana, from the top of his watch-tower, saw the flower of his warriors thus put to rout, his heart grew cold within him. Was this the fate that lay in store for him, the king of all the giants, the indomitable sovereign of Alengka, the ruler who had never known defeat? Had he survived so many dangers only to be finally crushed and mocked by such pocket-size creatures as these? Was he to be forced into submission to them? Never! Admittedly, the odds were against him, but he could still count on the loyalty of a few picked troops who could never forsake him.

All was not yet lost.

31. Kumbakarna is Roused from his Sleep

At this point Rawana was sorely tempted to murder Sinta and might well have done so, had not his evil design been thwarted by Trijata, Wibisana's beautiful daughter, who had grown to love Sinta as if she had been her own sister.

It then occurred to him that he had another brother to whom he might turn for help. This was Kumbakarna, the great sleeper. Unlike Rawana, Kumbakarna was not an outlaw by temperament. "Live and let live" was his motto. But for all that, he might be able to tip the balance in Rawana's favour. True, Rawana had never much cared for this lazy glutton of a brother, but now that he so badly needed his assistance, he quickly succeeded in overcoming his habitual dislike, and even went so far as to admit that he might sometimes have wronged him.

Now it was well known that Kumbakarna excelled his fellow-giants in almost every respect: he was taller and heavier; he was lazier and stronger; he was more tolerant and more humane. His appetite was prodigious: in nibbling at what was to him no more than a light snack he could easily out-eat a dozen hungry labourers. His drowsiness was a byword: the verb "to kumbakarnate" had gained general currency in the sense of "to have a long, deep sleep".

Rawana found him face downward in the shade of a spreading banyan tree. The ground beneath him heaved and trembled with his heavy, stertorous snoring. Now, a slumbering giant was of no use whatever to Rawana. His brother would have to be roused. It was perhaps a little unfortunate that no one had ever been known to possess sufficient strength to shake him into wakefulness, but Hin-

Kumbakarna

drajit had devised a method which experience had shown to b
effective. He stooped down and firmly grasped the coarse hair on

Kumbakarna's big toe. One mighty pull, and Kumbakarna let out a roar of pain. He felt as if his foot had been transfixed with a red-hot needle. He was on his feet in a twinkling, and stood there angrily shaking his unkempt mane of unruly red hair. In his annoyance he gnashed his teeth so violently that sparks flew off from him in all directions.

At first he flatly refused to help Rawana. "You've brought this on yourself," he growled, "and you're getting no better than you deserve. How often have I reminded you that 'they who have sown the wind shall reap the whirlwind'? You brainless idiot! All your life you've been wronging and harming your neighbours and getting away with it, and now the day of reckoning has caught you unprepared. I'm all against fighting innocent folks like Rama. It's only because we're of the same flesh and blood that I'm willing to join you in your last stand. We've neither of us lived particularly well, so I suppose it's up to us to prove that we can at least die well. Come on, then!" So saying, Kumbakarna stumbled grudgingly off towards the front line, closely followed by Rawana.

32. The Greatest Battle of All Time

After their first attack, the wanaras had taken a good rest so as to be ready for the next battle, which they were sure would be decisive. The forces of Alengka, too, were making their preparations. Maricha had fallen in the first encounter, Wibisana had gone over to the enemy, and thousands of their doughtiest warriors had already been killed or disabled. It was evident, therefore, that the giants' wisest plan of campaign would be to try to force the issue while the invaders were still recovering from their long journey and their strenuous exertions in the Battle of the Forest. All giants below the age of sixty were promptly ordered to the colours; in that way, it was hoped, a defensive force of sufficient size could be recruited. The pick of the troops were placed under the command of the most experienced generals — Hindrajit, Kumbakarna, Prahasta and Jambumangli.

When at last the war-gongs sounded, they began their ponderous advance, and the whole earth echoed to the tramp of marching feet.

But the wanaras under Rama were not content to wait in idleness for the enemy to launch his attack, but advanced with all speed to meet it. The two opposing armies were soon within earshot of each other. As they drew nearer, the clatter and clangour of their heavy equipment were carried far and wide through the stillness of the morning air, and the scurrying clouds of dust churned up by the weight of their armour had soon enveloped the whole countryside. Suddenly the two armies were face to face, and charging headlong forward with terrifying shouts and battle-cries, they fell upon each other with the utmost savagery.

In those ancient times it was custom for opposing generals to fight in single combat. Accordingly it fell out that Kumbakarna, that most gigantic of giants, was challenged by the slight and slender Lesmana. It was like seeing a heavyweight and a flyweight champion thrown together in the same ring. The spectators watched with bated breath, convinced that Lesmana must be crushed to powder in a matter of ·conds. They saw Kumbakarna's arms flailing furiously in a whirl of blows, any one of which would have spelled death for Lesmana, if only it had landed. As it was, he dodged them all, ducking and darting and bobbing and weaving and feinting and skipping and dancing round his puzzled adversary with all the adroitness of the strong-winged sikatan. At last Kumbakarna paused to get his breath back, his bulging eyes rolling balefully in their sockets, and fierce flames shooting from his panting mouth. The impudence of it! Was this slim youth to get the better of him? Was Kumbakarna's far-famed strength to fall victim to such trivial playfulness? His great bulk trembled with rage and from the depths of his brazen lungs he emitted a thunderous roar.

Then, opening his already gaping mouth as wide as he could, and stretching out his powerful arms to their fullest extent, he again charged forward with the irresistable impetus of a mad bull-elephant. Lesmana seemed doomed. His only hope now lay in his trusty bow. With quivering fingers he took careful aim. The onlookers craned their necks and strained their eyes as they peered through clouds of swirling dust and tried to make out what was happening. Lesmana was completely lost from view. Was this, then, to be the inglorious end of that sure-footed youth who had so bravely defied the giant's onslaught and escaped his tremendous swipes with such incredible speed and presence of mind? Would they never again enjoy the sight of his lithe and lissom movements or of his radiantly winning smile?

Just then a howl of anguish rent the air. Kumbakarna's huge bulk writhed in pain. For a moment, he lurched blindly forward, neither knowing nor caring where he was going. He tried to say something, but the words sounded strangled and half-formed. He turned, but stumbled. For Lesmana's magic arrow had buried itself in his throat.

It was in vain that he tugged and twitched and twisted in his efforts to dislodge it. His blood came spurting out in a crimson shower, and he staggered and reeled for a while like a drunkard, until at last he measured his length upon the warm, hard, dust-strewn, blood-be-spattered earth — a cold and lifeless corpse.

From the ranks of the apes there rose an ear-splitting yell of triumph unrestrained. Dancing with delight, the jubilant wanaras carried Lesmana shoulder-high back to the safety of their own lines.

33. Alengka's Total Defeat

While the struggle between Kumbakarna and Lesmana had been raging in one part of the field, other duels were being fought out elsewhere. Not least among these was that between Hindrajit, the Crown Prince of Alengka, and Hanuman, the courageous general of the apes, a pair well matched in size and strength alike, for both were seasoned fighters, and expert in the handling of wapons. For some time they continued to grapple with each other; but the longer they struggled, the clearer it became that neither had the extra margin of strength and skill needed to overcome his opponent.

Eventually, Hanuman decided that he must resort to a trick, and, disengaging himself from Hindrajit's vise-like grip, he took to his heels, as if in fear and Hindrajit at once gave chase. The Alengkan forces began to jeer at Hanuman as he kept on running, coming nearer and nearer towards the shelter of the forest, while constantly evading the deadly thrusts of Hindrajit, still in close pursuit. Yet this was no panic flight, but well-planned tactical withdrawal. Just as they reached the edge of the forest, Hindrajit, incensed at Hanuman's apparent cowardice, lunged forward at his throat. But, quick as lightning, Hanuman had sprung up on to an overhanging branch from which, a split second later, he had dived down on to Hindrajit's back, catching him completely off balance. Before the bewildered Prince quite knew what was happening, his head had been bitten clean off at the shoulders and lay rolling in the dust. Yet another burst of cheering arose from the serried ranks of the wanaras.

Meanwhile, at some distance from this bloody scene, Rawana had observed that the casualties among his own troops outnumbered those of the enemy by nearly ten to one and that more than half of his most trusted generals had already been slain. An icy chill of despair settled on his heart. But even now he was too proud to surrender. Better to die in freedom than survive in chains!

At that moment his attention was caught by the sight of someone speeding through the fray directly towards him. It was Rama, the commander-in-chief of the invading forces and his deadliest foe. No sooner had Rama come within shooting range than he began to shower down a hail of arrows upon Rawana, who, however, to his dismay, appeared unhurt by them. Yet the shots were not without effect, for they did force the giant to keep backing away and discouraged him from attempting a counter-attack. Rama therefore maintained his steady stream of arrows, before which Rawana continued to retreat, quite failing to notice that he was drawing steadily closer to a pair of rocks of most unusual formation. And, just as he backed in between them, these great rooks snapped together, like the jaws of a powerful trap, pinning him in a relentless grip. The more he struggled to free himself, the more firmly was he held, and there, for all his efforts to escape, he stayed and languished, doomed to suffer till the end of time for all the evil he had brought upon the world.

Strange to relate, those rocks were inhabited by the souls of the two daughters who he had once foully murdered and whose spirits had long been thirsting for an opportunity to avenge themselves upon their cruel, tyrannical father.

Seeing their leader thus immobilized, the other giants lost heart. What use was there in continuing an unjust war that had already cost them so many lives and mangled limbs? What point was there in keeping Sinta parted from her lawful husband? Accordingly, they threw down their weapons and surrendered.

Rama granted them a generous amnesty, and forbade that any of his followers should attempt to do them further harm.

34. Happy Ending

Rama then turned to thank Wibisana, whose help in guiding the military operations of the apes had been invaluable to him. To restore the good name of Alengka, which Rawana's misdeeds had so be smirched, a firm, just ruler would have to be appointed. No one could have been found more fit for that high office than Wibisana, to whom, accordingly, Rama now offered the crown, confident that, under his benevolent reign, Alengka would enjoy a new era of peace and plenty and prosperity.

When at last Rama found his beloved Sinta safe and sound and lovelier than over, he was happy beyond words, and Sinta's blissfully shining eyes gave proof that she was no less overjoyed at being reunited with her husband.

At this wonderful moment of reunion, Sinta and Rama had not forgotten the two friends who had done most to bring it about, i.e. Hanuman, whose daring had made Sinta's rescue possible, and Trijata, the beautiful daughter of Wibisana, who had sustained and comforted and constantly shielded Sinta against the advances of the love-sick Rawana throughout her long ordeal in captivity. What could have been more appropriate than to unite this noble couple in a marriage that would set the seal upon future friendship of their respective people? But, alas, such was not to be. Trijata, who had at first fallen in love with Lesmana, eventually married Jembawan, while Hanuman surprisingly took one of Rawana's wives — the stunningly beautiful Sayempraba — as his spouse.

The fourteen-year term of their banishment having just elapsed, there was no longer any obstacle to hinder Rama and Sinta from

Sinta   *Trijata*

returning to their native land, where Barata delightfully fulfilled his
promise to hand back the crown that he had kept in trust for his
long-exiled brother.

The whole realm of Kosala rejoiced to welcome home the handsome Rama and his lovely Queen. A triumphal procession was held in which all the victorious apes marched proudly by. In the midst of these gay columns, through streets festooned and garlanded with flowers, drove the golden state coach, from which Rama and Sinta smiled their happiness and their affection for their cheering subjects.

Under Rama's wise governance, the kingdom progressed from strength to strength, becoming daily more prosperous and more pleasant. Everything would grow well in its rich and fertile soil — everything, that is, except weeds — and the crops never failed to yield abundant harvests. Food and clothes were inexpensive, though always of fine quality. Never were those neat, bright streets defaced by any vestige of poverty, for all the inhabitants were well fed, well clothed, and comfortably housed. Domestic animals were gentle and well-behaved and never needed to be tied up at night. Quarrels and enviousness, theft and dishonesty, famine and disease, entirely disappeared from the land. How could they survive where all the citizens were animated by the spirit of friendship and cooperation and good neighbourliness?

Kosala continued to thrive and flourish as a great and glorious nation, and the memory of Rama, its wise and valiant king has ever been cherised and revered, and, please God, ever will be, until the very end of time.

As the last sounds of the gamelan music seem to hurry toward a final climax, the Dalang takes the "gunungan" from the left hand-side of the stage, gingerly makes it spin briefly before him, and eventually plants it firmly in an erect position in the banana-stem, as a signal that the nine-hour show had come to an end.

He then turns his head toward the weary musicians, who, falling in line with the Dalang, put down their tools by which they made the various intruments produce the multifarious sounds.

All is silent now, except that some of the musicians — knowing that freedom of action has been restored to them at last — now no longer try to repress their urge to yawn.

76

Seeing that everyone and everything seem to be all right now, the Dalang slowly gets to his feet. While adjusting his "ikat kepala" or head-cloth, he makes his way toward the inner part of the house, where he finds his host waiting for him. No sooner has he seated himself, than hot coffee is served. With a smile of satisfaction and gratitude the host then hands him the remainder of the agreed stipend.

Making the customary respectful bow, the Dalang finally says goodbye and returns to where the musicians and the woman singer are. From them, too, he takes leave, and with a sigh of relief prepares for his journey back home.

Both physically and spiritually exhausted but happy, the many-sided artist almost involuntarily brings back to mind everything that has happened during the past nine hours of his exacting show. A sensation of well-being takes hold of him when he remembers how well his audience appreciated his performance; how most of the spectators' eyes remained glued to the moving puppets; how well he managed to illicit guffaw upon guffaw from the audience through the carefully selected jokes which he dished up from time to time. And how they thoroughly enjoyed the masterful technique by which he made the opposing characters fight one another.

Meanwhile it will also occur to him how much gratitude he actually owes the leader of the musicians, i.e the "pengendang" or drummer. Because it was especially due to him that the still puppets really came to life. Whith his incredibly nimble fingers he managed to draw out even the most fantastic sounds by which the movements of the characters were accentuated.

And how about the singer? She, too, deserves a word of praise. Without her extensive repertoir of songs which were alternatively gay, moody, heart-warming or even soul-stirring as occasion demanded, his perfomance would not have attained the desired standard. She knew but too well when the Dalang would interrupt his narration in order to allow himself a moment's rest, and immediately she filled the gap with that type of song which was in harmony with the then prevailing mood, i.e. one of the three cardinal moods to be created by the orchestra during the nine hour span.

Yes, he also remembers how well the rebabplayer did. This time, too, he was as infallible as ever. And as to the rest of the musicians, he did not have any particular reason for complaint, except perhaps, to the address of the player of the big gongs. Though admittedly the latter did not too badly on the whole, the Dalang's trained ear could not fail to detect certain irregularities in his technique. There were namely times at which he struck the gongs either one split second too late or too early, and thus spoiling the otherwise perfect harmony. The Dalang promises himself to take the culprit to task some day for these little failings, because these might eventually harm his good reputation. In his view an excellent reputation is almost as precious a treasure as the American gold reserve at For Knox, Kentucky.

But on the whole the show was a success. There was no doubt about it. The response of the onlookers was enthusiastic throughout, which went to show that he has fully satisfied the spectators' highest expectations. Knowing this makes the Dalang almost happy beyond expression. For him, namely, the purpose of art is to entertain, and the essential purpose of life is to serve the community.

Finally he toys with the idea that his latest show might have brought him one step nearer his life's goal, i.e. to assist his country-men in their quest of the true significance of human existence.

RAMAYANA

Anotasi

1. Preparing for the Show

to prepare – menyiapkan
a show – pertunjukan, tontonan
a performance
an insect – serangga
unsteady – tak tetap
to cast – melemparkan
dazzling – menyilaukan
a screen – kelir, layar
a stage – panggung
leather – kulit
a puppet – wayang, boneka
a space – ruang
to pursue – mengejar
trial beats – pukulan percobaan
a mixture – campuran
an onlooker – penonton
to flock – datang berkumpul
eager – ingin sekali
reserved – disediakan, diperuntukkan
makes up for the loss – mengimbangi kerugian
to join – bersatu dengan, turut
a musician – pemain musik
seated cross-legged – duduk dengan kaki bersilang, sila (Jawa)
incense – kemenyan
to invoke – memanggil, meminta pertolongan
a favour – karunia, anugerah
the ancestors – nenek moyang
endurance – kesabaran
clarity – terang
nimbleness – kecerdasan
glibness – kelancaran
to fail – gagal
accurately – tepat
individual mannerisms – kebiasaan pribadi
to imitate closely – meniru dengan tepat
to some extent – agak sedikit
the prestige – pengaruh
the sacrificial offerings – upacara selamatan
to ward off – menangkis
interference – gangguan

evil spirits — semangat jahat
a cooked rice-cone — nasi tumpeng
to accompany — menyertai
spiced meats — gulai
to alter — mengubah
a device — kumpulan
to emphasize — mengutamakan
the clangour of clashing weapons — bunyi senjata yang membentur
presently — sebentar lagi
all purpose — serba guna
to represent — menandakan, mewakili
an abode — tempat tinggal
a huge obstacle — rintangan besar
pincers — japit, catut
the wick (of a lamp) — sumbu (lampu)

2. The Dalang

extraordinary — luar biasa, bukan main
antertainer — penghibur
to amuse — menyenangkan hati
physically — dari segi jasmaniah
the strain — ketegangan, susah-payah
to imagine — membayangkan
successive — berturut-turut
a wink of sleep — tidur barang sekejap mata
incessantly — terus-menerus
a joke — senda-gurau, kelakar
every now and then — sebentar-sebentar
to control — menguasai, memimpin
the audience — pendengar
to notice — memperhatikan
at intervals — sebentar-sebentar
to adjust — mengatur
to prevent — mencegah
to fade out — mati perlahan-lahan
he does not leave it at that — bukan itu saja yang diperbuatnya
small wonder — tidak mengherankan
to admire — mengagumi
to respect — menghormat
a source — sumber

enjoyment – kenikmatan
humour – humor, lelucon
to provide – memberikan
unsurpassed – tak ada taranya
usually – biasanya
as far as money is concerned – mengenai soal uang
satisfied – puas
relatively – jika dibandingkan dengan hal lain yang serupa
a sum – sejumlah uang
to compare – membandingkan
the community – masyarakat
a reward – hadiah
exacting – berat, banyak tuntutannya
decently – agak miskin
sparkling – gemerlapan
a miracle – keajaiban
fantastic – menakjubkan
cramp – kekejangan

3 The Show Begins

is set for – siap untuk
simultaneously – serentak
soulful – penuh perasaan
a rap – ketukan
to remove – mengangkat
vast – luas
glorious – agung, jaya, mulia
fertile – subur
crops – tanaman di sawah/ladang
harvests – panen, hasil tanaman
inexpensive – murah
domestic animals – binatang jinak
mutual help – bantu membantu gotong-royong
the citizen – warga negara
a warm invitation – undangan/sambutan hangat
supper – makan malam
a comfortable lodging – penginapan yang menyenangkan
lofty – tinggi
prosperous – makmur
timber – kayu yang dapat dipakai ramuan
marble – marmar

extensive — luas
to surround — mengelilingi
the shrubs — semak-semak
various plumage — bermacam jenis (bulu)
crystal-pure — bening sekali
the lily-ponds — telaga bakung

4. King Dasarata Gives up the Throne

to give up — melepaskan
in perfect harmony — amat rukun
constant practice — latihan tetap
unmatched — tak ada taranya
to pierce — menembus
unequalled — tak ada bandingnya
never failing — tidak pernah mengecewakan
in his nineties — berusia antara 90 dan 100 th, jadi 91, 92 . . ., 99 tahun
the spirit is strong, but the flesh is weak — kehendak hati memeluk gunung, apa
    daya tangan tak sampai
fatigued — amat payah, letih, lelah
heir — ahli waris
successor — pengganti
to succeed — menggantikan
crowning — penobatan
event — peristiwa
invariable — tidak berubah-ubah
an important epoch — waktu/peristiwa penting
aged — lanjut usia
to decorate — menghias
look forward to — ingin akan
magnificent — indah, bagus
reach new heights — mencapai puncak-puncak kejayaan baru
destined — ditakdirkan

5. A Dark Cloud on the Horizon

grudge — dendam
a cherished wish — keinginan/kehendak yang diharapkan
to ascend — menaiki

84

a throne – tahta, singgasana
a realm – kerajaan
an age-old tradition – adat-istiadat/tradisi yang telah berakar
precedence –. didahulukan
to bear – memikul, menahan
succession – penggantian
successor – pengganti
to abdicate the throne – turun takhta
to rack one's brains – memutar otak
to accomplish – menyelesaikan, melakukan
ambition – hasrat maju, cita-cita
to torture – menyiksa
anxiety – kecemasan
to neglect – mengabaikan
faithful – setia
sly – licik
a hag – wanita tua
to commit a crime – melakukan kejahatan
to console – menghibur
brilliant – cermelang
to flash – bergerak secepat kilat
cunning satisfaction – kepuasan penuh tipu muslihat
in honour of – guna menghormati
to despair – putus asa
may yet be fulfilled – masih dapat terkabul
to change one's mind – berganti pikiran, berubah niat
to announce – mengumumkan
faint – lemah
hitherto – sampai sekarang
to claim – menuntut
indulgence – memberi hati
heartfelt gratitude – perasaan terima kasih yang sungguh-sungguh
to avail oneself – menggunakan

6. Kekayi Claims the King's Reward

an excuse – alasan, dalih
crowned – dinobatkan
powerful – ampuh, perkasa
ungrateful – tak kenal terima kasih
a creature – makhluk

puzzled — bingung
a reward — hadiah, ganjaran
I take it that . . . — saya kira bahwa . . .
suspicion — kecurigaan
ancestors — leluhur, nenek-moyang
to suppress a yawn — menindas kuap (kantuk)
to utter — mengucapkan
a chest — dada, peti
to groan — mengeluh
to collect oneself — meneguhkan hati
to flush — menjadi merah di muka
flushed with anger — merah mukanya karena marah
cruel — kejam
selfish — dengki
disgraceful — hina, memalukan
to persist — berkeras kepala
tru to one's word — menepati janji

7. Rama's Banishment

a request — permohonan
through no fault of his own — bukan karena salahnya
unsuspected — tak disangka
a trap — perangkap
skilful — berpengalaman
to inflict — menghukum
an exile — pembuangan, pengasingan
to forswear one's oath — mengingkari sumpahnya
a perjurer — penyumpah palsu
to reflect — merenungkan, membayangkan
agonizing dilemma — pemilihan sukar yang menyiksa
reluctant — enggan
to resolve — memutuskan
a coronation — penobatan
to issue — mengeluarkan
stunned — terkejut, taajub, kagum, bingung
like a bolt from the blue — tak terduga-duga sama sekali
dumbfounded — tercengang
misfortune — celaka, nasib buruk
to yield — menyerah
a pledge — jaminan, kesanggupan

inviolable -- tak dapat dilanggar
to violate – melanggar
touching – mengharukan
to rush after – berlari, mengejar
to assert – menyatakan, menerangkan
to deprive – merampas
inheritance – warisan, pusaka
to urge -- mendesak
a subject – warga negara
to obey – menaati, mematuhi
there can be no question of that – hal itu tak usah diragukan, itu barang sudah
    pasti
to bless – memberkati
to sob – menangis tersedu-sedu
to stride on toward the gate – melangkah menuju pintu gerbang
to embrace tenderly – memeluk dengan lemah lembut
heart rending – amat mengharukan

8. *Dasarata Dies of Grief*

grief – dukacita
to grieve – berdukacita
to shed – menumpahkan,   mengalirkan
to sob – menangis tersedu-sedu
to decrease – berkurang
to increase – bertambah
to share – mengambil bagian
to persist – keras kepala
to give in – menyerah, menuruti
to blame – menyalahkan
to rage – mengamuk
the strain – tekanan keadaan, kegentingan
to pass away – meninggal, mangkat
to go into mourning – berkabung
pretence – pura-pura
inwardly – dalam batinnya
had in store for her – ditakdirkan baginya
dismay – putus asa, kesedihan
flatly refused – menolak mentah-mentah
unworthy – tak patut
wrath – amarah

to urge – mendesak
to wheedle – membujuk
to budge – bergerak
furious – sangat marah
by hook or by crook – dengan jalan apa saja
to overlook – melupakan
in advance – sebelumnya

9. Barata's Noble Attitude

noble – mulia, luhur
the attitude – sikap
the funeral rites – upacara penguburan
in search of – mencari
to catch up – menyusul
a grievous loss – kehilangan yang menyedihkan
to insist – mendesak, berkeras
to assume – menerima
the country affairs – urusan negara
to share – membagi
to argue – berdebat, bertengkar mulut
an argument – alasan
to strengthen one's obligation – memperkuat kewajibannya
to resolve – memutuskan
to resign – menerima
the fate – nasib
to propose – mengusulkan
a deputy – wakil
pending – selama
a kinsman – saudara
a godspeed – selamat jalan
temporary – sementara
steadfastly – tetap, tabah.
to reject – menolak
an importunate and oft-repeated advice – nasehat yang merepotkan dan sering
    diulang
attempting to usurp –.berusaha merebut
the prerogative – hak luar biasa
authority – kekuasaan
severe – keras
to perish – tewas, mendapat celaka

a trio — tiga serangkai
threaded their way — menempuh jalan berliku-liku
to be accustomed — biasa
the amenity — keramah-tamahan
amid — di tengah-tengah
the dense, lush vegetation — tumbuh-tumbuhan tebal dan berair
to distuinguish — membedakan, mengenal
edible — dapat dimakan
fowl — unggas, ayam, itik
to quench — menghilangkan
a species — macam, jenis
juicy — banyak airnya
gradually — dengan perlahan-lahan
to adapt oneself to — menyesuaikan diri dengan
the environment — sekitarnya
to ache — merasa sakit
satin — sutera yang mengkilap
to escape — melarikan diri, terlepas
it could not escape their notice — mereka tahu juga
sorely — sangat, amat
to repose — mengaso

10. Rama Builds a Forest Home for Sinta

to be keenly aware — sadar sekali
suffering — penderitaân
an exile — pengasingan, orang buangan
an abundance — melimpah-limpah banyaknya
a column — tiang
leafy — rimbun
threat — ancaman
to hover — terkatung-katung di udara
an eagle — burung elang
to keep company — mengawani
in search of food — mencari makanan
special arrangments — persiapan khusus
a harm — kejahatan
to establish — mendirikan
invisible — tak kelihatan
under no circumstances — bagaimanapun juga
a sheath — sarung senjata

unbearable – tak tertahankan
to wait on – melayani
to hold back – menahan
to cheer up – menghibur
on one occasion – pada suatu kesempatan
to neglect – mengabaikan
to starve – mati kelaparan
doubtless – pasti, tentu
in the course of time – sementara waktu berjalan
a zoo – kebun binatang
to entrust – mempercayakan
to provide – memberi
absorbing – mengasyikkan
an occupation – kesibukan
the charge – pemeliharaan
ample – luas
to wade – menyeberangi
honey – madu
for the picking – tinggal memetik
to all appearances – rupanya, melihat gelagatnya
surface – permukaan
existence – kehidupan

11. Rawana Discovered their Hiding Place

in succession – berturut-turut
civilization – peradaban
to forsake – meninggalkan
observed – diamat-amati
giants – raksasa
dreaded – dahsyat
without – luar
rotten – busuk
within – dalam
blood shot – kemerah-merahan
bushy – tebal
a cavern – gua
a monster – raksasa
a nightmare – mimpi yang menakutkan
despicable – hina
dishonest – tak jujur

90

uncommonly — luar biasa
greedy — serakah, rakus
wicked — jahat
anguish — takut, duka-cita
a victim — korban
inhuman — tak seperti manusia, kejam
soulless — tak berperasaan
vicious — jahat
a barbarian — orang biadab
to inhabit — mendiami
the trespassers — pelanggar-pelanggar
to trust — mempercayai

12. Caught Napping

to nap — tidur sebentar
sweltering — terik
close at hand — dekat
to spot — mengetahui
a foliage — daun-daunan
a prey — mangsa
a wasp — tawon
to alight — hinggap
to depart — pergi
to lack — tak mempunyai, kekurangan
dramatic — dramatis
meditation — semadi, renungan
prayer — doa, sembahyang
to consult — minta nasihat
the chatter — ocehan
grave — pudar dan tenang, tidak bergembira
incarnation — penitisan, penjelmaan
take my word for it — percayalah akan kebenaran kata saya
to molest — menganggu
contempt — sikap menghina
miserable — hina, celaka
a coward — penakut
to scare — menakut-nakuti
to involve — melibatkan
to sting — menyengat
rose in violent anger — menjadi amat marah

a dagger — pisau belati
to give in — menyatakan sanggup, menyerah
to plot — sekongkol

13. The Golden Deer

a pet — binatang timangan
special — istimewa
a squirrel — bajing, tupai
a source — sumber
the amusement — kesenangan
a creature — makhluk
not the slightest — sedikitpun tidak
to polish — menggosok
shiny — mengkilap
tiny — kecil sekali
the attention — perhatian
attracted — tertarik
a coat — kulit
charmed — terpesona, tertarik sekali
to exclaim — berseru
excitedly — gembira, gugup
a darling — kekasih
royal — kerajaan (yang bertalian dengan raja)
to worry — bersusah hati
to avoid — menghindari
the astonishment — keheranan
apparent — terang
on the contrary — malahan
to frisk — meloncat girang
to frolick — meloncat bersuka ria
out of reach — di luar jangkauan
the hindlegs — kaki belang
gracefully — dengan lemah gemulai
a display — pertunjukan, pameran
elegance — lemah gemulai
at stake — dalam pertaruhan
to utter — mengucapkan
fleeing — melarikan diri

14. Rama is Lured Away

to lure — memikat, menggoda
a brother-in-law — ipar laki-laki
almighty — maha kuasa
a prize — hadiah
gradually — berangsur-angsur
suspicious — curiga
a victim — korban
a trick — muslihat
to become evident — menjadi nyata
deliberately — dengan sengaja
separated — terpisah
alive — hidup
thereupon — sesudah itu
to take aim — membidik
an arrow — anak panah
strange sight — aneh
a spot — tempat
to writhe — meliuk
to twitch — meregang-regang urat
a fatal wound — luka parah
to summon — mengundang, menuntut, memanggil
uncanningly — mengerikan
an urgent cry — teriakan yang mendesak
distress — kesengsaraan, sesal, duka-cita
apprehensive — khawatir, takut
to lose one's way — kehilangan arah
to utter — mengucapkan
pricked up her ears — berusaha keras untuk mendengar
to shout — meneriak, berseru
to soothe — menenangkan, membujuk
to assure — meyakinkan
to come off worse — gagal
any trial of strength and valour — tiap usaha kekuatan dan keberanian
to heed — memperhatikan
to urge — mendesak
the aid — pertolongan
in desperation — karena putus asa
to taunt — mengejek, menghina
an accusation — tuduhan
to endure — menderita
to scathe — melukai

to sting — stung — stung — menyengat, merangsang
to insist — mendesak
to lock — mengunci
on any account — dalam keadaan bagaimanapun
to speed-sped-sped — segera, tergopoh-gopoh
to speed away — menghilang dengan segera

15. Sinta Kidnapped by Rawana

to kidnap — menculik
relieved — lega
to the rescue — pergi untuk menolong
serious — sungguh-sungguh, hebat
foolish — bodoh
whim — tingkah, iseng
defenceless — tak berdaya
a blast of wind — hembusan angin mendadak
at intervals — sebentar-sebentar
mysterious — bersifat rahasia
to enquire — bertanya
to shelter — berlindung
panic-stricken — kalang kabut, amat gugup
to pretend — pura-pura
weak — lemah
vigorous — kuat
in grave danger — dalam bahaya maut
gruesome — ngeri
to gather — mengumpulkan
to prepare — mempersiapkan
to escape — melarikan diri
to swoon — pingsan
towering — amat tinggi
to allow — mengizinkan
to introduce — memperkenalkan
to be quite frank — untuk berterus terang
to confess — mengakui
to escort — mengantar, mengawal
possible — mungkin
heroic — gagah perkasa
destined — ditakdirkan
a realm — kerajaan

to retort – menjawab
a leer – lirikan
it is no use – tiada gunanya
presently – segera setelah
to recover consciousness – sadar dari pingsan
downward – ke bawah
to catch a glimpse – menangkap/melihat selintas
a ravine – jurang

16. Jathayu to the Rescue

terrific – hebat
a rate – kecepatan
a landscape – pemandangan alam
blurred – kabur
indistinct – kabur
to obey – menurut(i)
an impulse – bisikan hati
a necklace – kalung
to exceed – melampaui
earthly – keduniaan
the bounds – batas-batas
misfortune – nasib buruk, celaka
pest – penyakit pest
epidemic – wabah
the prosperity – kemakmuran
well-being – keadaan baik, keselamatan
benefit – faedah, untung
absorbed – asyik berfikir
faithful – setia
to cruise – menjelajah
the sworn enemy –. musuh tujuh turunan
to descend – turun
horror – perasaan ngeri
a captive – tawanan
to expose to danger – membahayakan
height – tinggi (nama benda)
the odds were against him – perbedaan dalam keadaan merugikan baginya
to survive – tetap hidup
a talisman – jimat

made up his mind — memutuskan
an alternative — pilihan, jalan lain
to grapple — berkelahi
chanced — kebetulan
an arch enemy — musuh tujuh turunan
a dagger — pisau belati
at the top of her voice — sekeras-kerasnya
no sooner ... than — baru saja
a bill — paruh
latter's — kedua, terakhir
firmly driven — ditancapkan dengan keras
to drive - drove - driven — mengarahkan, memasukkan
heart-rending — memilukan
a shriek — pekik
anguish — sakit,duka-cita
a layer — lapisan
a resounding thud — gebuk bergema
gaping — lebar lagi dalam

17. Rama in Despair

in despair — putus asa
a victim — korban
sincerely — sepenuh hati
an instruction — perintah, petunjuk
anxiety — kecemasan, kekhawatiran
cast down — ditujukan ke arah
gave a start — terkejut
opposite — berlawanan
immediately — dengan segera
to sense — merasa, seakan-akan mengetahui
to approach — mendekati
cupped his hand — kedua belah tangan dijadikan corong
scarcely — hampir tidak
failed to observe his words — tak berhasil mentaati perintahnya
to stare — menatap
the ensuing silence — kesunyian yang menyusul
eloquent — pandai bicara
reproachful — kesal hati
took to his heels — pergi
in hot pursuit — cepat mengejar

deserted — sunyi
no doubt — tak sangsi lagi
hostile — bermusuhan
tormented — disiksa
beloved — tercinta

18. On the Right Trail

a trail — bekas, jejak, jalan
to force — memaksa
onattended — tanpa penjagaan, tanpa perhatian
securely — terjamin
to venture — mengambil risiko
forth — selanjutnya
bewildered — bingung
to stumble against — terantuk kepada
limply — lemah sekali
to tremble — mengigil
to stroke — mengusap-usap, mengelus-elus
with great effort — dengan susah payah
gasped — berkata dengan terputus-putus
to quiver — menggigil
motionless — tak bergerak
to bless — memberkati
heaven — sorga
farewell — sclamat tinggal
a swamp — rawa
sore — sakit
the slopes of a mountain — lereng gunung
a stronghold — benteng
a race — suku bangsa
a guard — penjaga
an outpost — pos terdepan
bluish — kebiru-biruan
respectful — hormat
the territory — daerah
to reveal — melahirkan, memberitahukan

19. Rama Gained a Powerful Ally

an ally — sekutu
questioning — pertanyaan
to declare — menyatakan
indeed — sesungguhnya
rightful — berhak
to establish — mendirikan, menetapkan
to recover — merebut kembali, membebaskan, sembuh
a vein — urat
a heritage — warisan
to usurp — merebut, merampas
invulnerable — kebal, bertuah
a venture — pekerjaan susah
to requite — membalas
a favour — sokongan, pertolongan, kebaikan
to deserve — patut mendapat
single-handed — sendiri, dengan tak memerlukan pertolongan
to court — mencari, memancing
disaster — bencana
to overcome — mengalahkan
disposal — boleh memakai
fearless — tak kenal takut, berani
to bring up — membesarkan, mendidik
brought up — dibesarkan, dididik
justice will prevail — keadilan pasti menang
to resist — melawan
the guise — bentuk
to encounter — berjumpa
a manifest injustice — ketidak adilan yang nyata
an alliance — persekutuan, gabungan
without delay — tanpa tangguh, segera
to settle his account — menyelesaikan urusannya
confident — penuh kepercayaan, yakin
to overpower — mengalahkan
an opponent — lawan
his fondest dreams — cita-citanya

20. Sugriwa Defeats Subali

to reach without incident — sampai dengan selamat
impending — mengancam

98

promptly — segera
the scouts — pengintai
a rival — lawan bersaing
face to face — berhadapan
to glare — memandang dengan marah
fierce resentment — kebencian yang hemat
circling — melingkar
cautious — berhati-hati
to draw closer — mendekat
to erect — berdiri
to crouch — membungkuk
to bend-bent-bent — membengkok, melengkung
to bare — memperlihatkan
a fang — taring
a hiss — bunyi desis
to take the offensive — memulai penyerbuan
to lunge forward — maju cepat
to tear to shreds — mencabik-cabik, menyobek-nyobek
an adversary — musuh
wary — berhati-hati
mutual stalking — saling melangkah
to grip — memegang, menangkap
to lower — mengurangi
a guard — penjagaan
impatient — tidak sabar
to leap - lept - lept — meloncat
the throat — kerongkongan
to groan — mengerang, mengeluh
to grapple and wrestle — berkelahi dan bergulat
to twist — memutar
the rapid fury — kemarahan kencang
a whirl-wind — angin puyuh, lesus
harsh panting — engah kasar
the straining muscles — otot yang tegang
to wrench oneself free — melepaskan diri, membebaskan diri
to punch — mendorong
to pummel — menumbuk sampai biru, memukul keras
to choke — mencekik
insensibility — pingsan
to relish — menikmati
a momentary pause — istirahat seketika
to penetrate — menembus

the scaly flesh — kulit yang bersisik
ungainly — canggung, kaku
to reel — bergoyang
to totter — terhuyung-huyung
to collapse — runtuh
convulsive — kejang
a timely intervension — campur tangan yang tepat
in tokenof —sebagai tanda, menandakan
gratitude — terima kasih
to perish — mendapat celaka
a touching scene — pemandangan yang mengharukan
an expulsion — pengusiran
in a body — serentak
to pay homage — menyatakan hormat
oath of loyality — sumpah setia
the tyrannous regime — cara memerintah sewenang-wenang
a banquet — pesta perjamuan
a restoration — perbaikan, pemulihan
righteous — adil

21. Hanuman Volunteers to Visit Alengka

to volunteer — mengajukan diri secara sukarela
nobly — dengan baik hati
to live up to — menepati
to assemble — mengumpulkan
the counsellors — penasihat
minor — kecil, kurang penting
an enterprise — peristiwa kejadian
actual — yang sesungguhnya
to reconnoitre — mengintai
to ascertain — menentukan, menetapkan
exact — tepat
a location — tempat, letak
to discover — mendapati, mengetahui
to posses — memiliki
imprisoned — dipenjarakan
eager — ingin sekali
to withdraw — mengundurkan diri
a quarrel — pertengkaran
they came to blows — mereka saling berhantam

100

to acknowledge — mengakui
superiority — keunggulan
an intruder — orang melanggar
was at stake — dalam pertaruhan
welfare of mankind — kesejahteraan kemanusiaan
to determine — menentukan
the enthusiasm — gelora semangat
to vow — bersumpah
the whereabouts — tempat diam, kira-kira di mana
to prove — membuktikan
an imposter — pembohong
to bid - bade - bidden — mengucapkan
stout — berani

22. Hanuman Encounters Wikateksi

certain — pasti
reliable — dapat dipercaya
to take the risk — mengambil risiko
heading due south — langsung menuju ke selatan
the obstacles — rintangan
to avail oneself of — mempergunakan
the foam-flecked surf — gelombang yang berbintik-bintik busa
incessantly — tiada putusnya
the coastal cliffs — batu karang lancip berbentuk tulang iga
grim — suram
to indicate — menunjukkan
unobserved — tak ketahuan
to submerge — menyelam
formidable — hebat
a guard — penjaga
immense — luar biasa besar
dimension — ukuran
to gulp — menelan
a whale — ikan paus
a morsel — sesuap
chanced to tempt — kebetulan menggoda
concealed — bersembunyi
swivelling — memusar
to protrude — menjulang

surface – permukaan
on guard – melakukan penjagaan
suspicious – curiga
to arouse – membangkitkan
puzzled – bingung
cavernous – seperti gua
a cavern – gua
to suck – menyedot, mengisap
inexorable – keras, tak mengenal ampun
frenzied – gila
the eddying turbulance – pusaran air yang bergelora
giddy – pusing
the howling – lolong, raung
stupendous – mengherankan
a blast – letusan
humid – basah

23. Hamunan Puts an End to Wikateksi's Life

to escape – terlepas, lolos
to exasperate – menimbulkan kebencian, memarahkan
a pit – lobang
the stifling depths – kedalaman yang pengap
a volcano – gunung berani
to entomb – menguburkan
a cavern – gua
slippery – licin
an eel – belut
to groan – berkeluh kesah
to conclude – menyimpulkan
to swallow – menelan
a monster – binatang yang dahsyat
to venture – memberanikan diri
to imagine – membayangkan
the horror – perasaan ngeri
a stomache – perut
to confine – mengurung
a hold – ruang di bawah geladak kapal. Di sini : perut
with all his might – dengan sekuat tenaga
to resign to one's fate – menyerah kepada nasib
to expand – membesarkan

102

to swell — membengkak
to captive — menawan
a captor — orang yang menawan
a torment — siksaan
fury — marah besar
to scramble — merangkak dengan susah payah
clear of — keluar dari
to rejoice — bergembira-ria
to avoid — menghindari
scattered — terserak-serak
the remnants — sisa
flotsam — bekas-bekas kapal yang terapung di laut
to leap — meloncat
an incident — kejadian

24. Hanuman Arrives in Alengka

to admire — mengagumi
fertile — subur
a meadow — padang rumput
unruly — sudah diatur
the crops — hasil, panen
a delight — kesenangan
to distinguish — mengenal
to loom up — timbul
to scale a wall — melompati tembok
an enchanting view — pemandangan yang mempesonakan
broad — lebar
the stately avenues — jalan-jalan raya besar
curiously — jarang, ajaib
marble — marmar
a tower — menara
a cupola — kubbat
to enroll — membentang
gaze — pemandangan
fatigue — capai, lelah
precious — berharga, teliti
glum-looking — kelihatan muram
peculiarly — aneh
ordinary — biasa
a screen — tabir, tirai, geber

to investigate — menyelidiki
to poke — menyodorkan
a couch — dipan
no one but him — hanya dia

25. Hanuman Makes Good Use of his Time

an exploration — penyelidikan
an arsenal — gudang senjata
stored — tersimpan
a women's quarter — tempat tinggal wanita
distinct from — berbeda dengan
exquisite — terpilih, bagus sekali
a carpet — permadani, babut
the strairs — tangga rumah
a trace — jejak
to abandon — meninggalkan
a quest — pencarian
a rooster — ayam jantan
dawn — fajar
to tidy — membereskan
a thoroughfare — jalan raya
fairly — agak
to spoil — merusak, merugikan, mengecilkan
on all fours — merangkak
to clamber up — memanjat
luxuriant — rimbun, berlimpah-limpah
the foliage — daun-daunan
to snatch some rest — beristirahat sebentar
to stretch — mengulurkan
laden — penuh, dimuati
to chat — bercakap-cakap, mengobrol
to assume — menduga
to slip down — meluncur ke bawah
the extraordinary beauty — kecantikan yang luar biasa
a handsome reward — hadiah agak banyak
the imagination — angan-angan
to perch — duduk
a bough — dahan besar, cabang
sufficiently — cukup
recover from surprise — mengatasi keheranan
to withdraw-withdrew-withdrawn — kembali, mundur

26. Hanuman's Great Moment

dusk — senja
secretly — secara rahasia, diam-diam
a device — rencana
to convince — meyakinkan
to mingle — mencampur
relief — perasaan lega
to observe — memperhatikan
to overhear — kebetulan mendengar, mendengar-dengarkan
a message — amanat, berita
to deliver — menyampaikan
to gain — memperoleh, mendapat
in public — di muka umum, terang-terangan
unsuspecting — tak menaruh curiga, tak menyangka
a host — tuan rumah
overlooked — melihat dari atas
to howl — melolong, meraung
a yell — teriak
to abduct — menculik
a sin — dosa
the populace — rakyat jelata
to uproot — mencabut seakar-akarnya
to brandish — mengayunkan
a club — gada, tongkat
to batter — memukulkan
an edifice — bangunan
take to one's heels — lari tunggang langgang
lofty — tinggi, mulia
to swear - swore - sworn — bersumpah
to roast — memanggang
alive — hidup-hidup
out of harm's way — jauh dari bahaya
the crown-prince — putera mahkota
to reel — terhuyung-huyung
a shaft — panah
to lose balance — kehilangan keseimbangan
to plunge headlong — jatuh dengan kepala ke bawah
a multitude — banyak, sejumlah besar
a warrior — perajurit

27. The Attempt to Burn Hanuman Alive

an attempt – usaha
the thriumph – kemenangan
lamed – lumpuh
dazed – tak dapat berfikir jelas, bingung
the fetter – belenggu kaki
the chains – rantai
to load – memuat
to gnash – menggertakkan
vindictive rage – marah dengan keinginan membalas dendam
rapid – cepat
dense – tebal, padat
throng – mendesak
a spectator – penonton
frenzied – gila
to witness – menyaksikan
to gloat over – menelan dengan mata
to appeal for help – meminta pertolongan
schorching flame – nyala yang menghanguskan
swirling – berpolang-paling
a column – tiang besar
increasingly difficult – semakin sukar
to breathe – bernafas
to bestir oneself – mengusahakan diri
contrived – mencari akal
superhuman – melebihi tenaga manusia
to fling - flung - flung – melemparkan
the merry-makers – orang-orang yang bersuka ria
to snatch – merenggut
a pile – timbunan
a shriek – pekik
miraculous – ajaib
to wear off – melepaskan, menghilangkan
to wear-wore-worn – memakai
to pois – bersikap tenang, mencari keseimbangan
an edge – pinggir
a ghost – hantu
an avenger – pembalas dendam
to fan – mengipas
a raid – penyerbuan
to assure – meyakinkan diri
distressed – menyedihkan

28. Hanuman Bridges the Strait

content — puas
a mission — utusan
reprobate — durjana, bangsat
moved to tears — amat terharu
to release — membebaskan, melepaskan
odious — menjengkelkan, menimbulkan benci
to adopt — mengangkat (anak)
to confer — menganugerahkan
the honour — kehormatan
speechless — tak dapat berkata
immense gratification — kepuasan hati yang luar biasa
a campaign — peperangan
to bear arms — memikul senjata
the morale — semangat
scarcely — hampir tidak
keen anticipation — perasaan hati yang sungguh-sungguh
decisive — diputuskan, bersifat menentukan
a crime — kejahatan
insensate — tak berperasaan, tak berperikemanusiaan
to turn the tide — membalikkan keadaan
the tide — air pasang
wasted — disia-siakan
to be concious of — yakin akan
in close columns — dalam barisan yang padat
a guide — penunjuk jalan
an ensign — panji, tanda, lambang
a pennant — umbul-umbul
to flutter — berkibar
to glitter — berkilau
to glint — berseri, berkilap
inexorable — tak mengenal ampun
abrupt — tiba-tiba
to surge — berombak, bergelombang
the pounding surf — ombang-ombak yang menumbuk
the chasm — darab, jurang
out of the question — tak mungkin sama sekali
the violence of its currents — kekerasan arus
the sharpness — ketajaman
the cruel, jagged rocks — batu karang ganas yang tajam
mutual confidence — saling percaya
mutual aid — tolong-menolong

countless – tidak terhitung
to conquer – menaklukkan, mengalahkan
to set the pace – memulai
a huge boulder – batu bulat yang amat besar
to hurl – melemparkan
to strew-strewed-strewn/strewed – menaburkan, menyerakkan
stout – kuat, berani
a tree-trunk – batang pohon
a tendril – dahan
shale – batu licin
shingle – batu kerikil
the craggy cliffs – batu karang yang curam
a causeway – tanggul
to emerge – timbul, tampil, terbentuk
to toil – bekerja keras
the menage of nature – ancaman alam
to snatch – merebut, mencakup

29. The Start of Rawana's Nightmare

a nightmare – mimpi yang menakutkan
impassable – tidak dapat diseberangi
to set foot – menginjakkan kaki
uninvited – tidak diundang
embittered – sakit hati
aware – sadar
impregnable – tak dapat dipungkiri
the isolation – isolasi, penyendirian, pemisahan
a century – satu abad
a vague, dim memory – kenangan kabur dan gelap
to bribe – memberi suap
to bully – suka memarahi
to cross his mind – melintasi pikirannya
to fancy – mengira, menggambarkan, mengkhayalkan
to exist – ada
merely – semata-mata
a fondly cherised illusion – angan-angan yang diharapkan dan disukai
to retain – dipertahankan
a despotic authority – kekuasaan kejam
unopposed – tak ada yang menentang

108

serenely — tenang, terang
an intruder — yang mengganggu
impunity — tidak mendapat hukuman
the smouldering ruins — reruntuhan yang membara
to ruin — menjadikan reruntuhan (puing)
shrewd — cerdas, berotak tajam
to guess — menerka
to pave the way — merintis jalan
full scale — besar-besaran
an invasion — penyerbuan
a spy — mata-mata
to ferret out — mengusut, mencari keterangan
defences — pertahanan
to pant — terengah-engah
in agony — dalam sengsara
to encamp — berkemah
to give vent — mengeluarkan pendapat
obscenely — bicara kotor, caci maki
to reproach — mencela, menyalahkan
to be alerted — berjaga-jaga
a delay — penundaan
forthwith — seketika itu juga
resentfully — mendendam
to disapprove of — tak membenarkan, mencela
the courage — keberanian
to challenge — menantang
high time — sudah waktunya
in plain terms — terus terang
an elected spokesman — jurubicara yang dipilih
tactfully — dengan bijaksana
to abduct — melarikan, menculik
to provoke — menyebabkan
to invade — menyerbu
a bloodshed — pertumpahan darah
to avert — menghindarkan
the assembled commanders — panglima yang terhimpun
to struck — menampar
unforgivable — tak dapat diampuni
an insult — penghinaan
to lead to — mengakibatkan
to lead-led-led — menuju
ultimately — akhirnya, kesudahannya
to desert — melarikan diri
to join — bergabung

30. The First Clash

a defender – pembela diri
streaming out – mengalir ke luar
to intent - bermaksud
a pitched battle – perang beraturan
a reconnaissance patrol – pasukan pengintai
the fringes – pinggir
the astonishment – keheranan
where on earth – di mana gerangan
an eerie screech – pekik mengerikan
in ambush – dalam pengadangan, dalam perangkap
to swing-swang-swung – berayun
to strike-struck-strick – memukul
the opponents – lawan
tranguil – tenang
a cacophony – bunyi yang tak enak kedengaran
to moan – mengaduh
to grunt – bersungut-sungut, merajuk
unaccustomed – tidak biasa
the warfare – perang
taken by surprise – disergap
an assailant – penyerbu, lawan
an annihilating blow – pukulan yang memusnahkan
viciously – bengis, tajam, kejam
the cafl – buah betis (kaki)
sprawling – terbadai
wel aimed – dibidik dengan tepat
beyond the reach – di luar jangkauan
perplex – bingung
cunning – cerdik, banyak tipu muslihat
an attack – serangan
to demoralize – menghilangkan semangat
sporadic – jarang terdapat
an assault – serangan, serbuan
to harass – meletihkan, melelahkan, menggoda
the tacties – siasat
swift – cepat
elusive – bersifat menghindari, mengelak
dawn – dini hari
wholly – sama sekali
at the mercy – nasibnya bergantung kepada kemurahan (orang lain)
to seek-sought-sought – mencari

110

refuge — perlindungan
mauled — cedera
rallied together — bersatu kembali
to beat a retreat — mundur, lari
withdrew to shelter — mundur berlindung
in order to — guna, untuk
the flower — arus
to put to rout — lari tunggang langgang
indomitable — tidak dapat dikalahkan
the sovereign — kedaulatan
a defeat — kekalahan
to crush — menghancurkan
to mock — mengejek, mengolok-olokkan
pocket-size — ukuran saku, kecil sekali
submission — takluk, tunduk
admittedly — memang, harus diakui
picked troops — pasukan pilihan
to loose-lost-lost — hilang

31. Kumbakarna is Roused from his Sleep

tempted — tergoda, ingin
to thwart — merintangi, menghalang-halangi
had grown to love her — akhirnya menjadi cinta kepadanya
it occured to him — ia teringat bahwa
the balance — keseimbangan
in his favour — menguntungkan baginya
a glutton — pelahap, orang yang terlalu banyak makan
habitual — biasa
even went so far as to admit — sampai-sampai mengaku
to wrong — memperlakukan tidak adil
in every respect — dalam segala hal
tolerant — sabar
humane — berperikemanusiaan
prodigious — hebat, luar biasa
to out-eat — mengalahkan dalam soal makan
to drowse — mengantuk
a byword — peribahasa
spreading — rimbun
the stertorous snoring — mendengkur
slumbering — pengantuk
effective — tepat, berhasil, manjur
to stoop down — menundukkan badan

111

to transfix — menembus, menusuk
in a twinkling — dalam sekejap mata
annoyance — terganggu
a spark — bunga api
flatly refused — menolak mentah-mentah
to deserve — sepatutnya mendapat
brainless — tak berotak, bodoh
the reckoning — perhitungan
innocent — tak berdosa
die well — mati secara jantan
grudgingly — setengah hati

32. The Greatest Battle of all Time

decisive — bersifat menentukan
doughtiest — paling berani
evident — terang, nyata
the issue — perjuangan
the strenuous exertions — usaha sungguh-sungguh
ordered to the colours — diperintahkan memanggul senjata
to recruit — memperkuat
a command — perintah
ponderous — berat
the tramp — derap kaki, langkah
in idleness — bermalas-malasan
to launch — melancarkan
within ear shot — dalam jarak pendengaran
the heavy equipments — senjata berat
to churn up — mengaduh
an armour — baju besi
to envelope — membungkus, menyelubungi
a savage — buas, biadab
ancient times — jaman kuno
the custom — adat istiadat
fight in single combat — berkelahi seorang lawan seorang, perang tanding
fell out — terjadilah
to challenge — menantang
heavy-weight — kelas berat
fly-weight — kelas ringan
a ring — gelanggang tinju
to crush — menumbuk, menghantam
the powder — bubuk, tepung

112

to flail — menebas
the adroitness — ketangkasan
impudent — tidak tahu malu
to fall victim to — menjadi korban daripada
trivial — tak berarti, biasa
brazen — sombong
the irresistable impetus — kekuatan yang tak dapat dihalangi
to quiver — menggetar
the onslaught — serangan ganas
the lithe and lissom movements — gerakan yang lincah dan tangkas
a winning smile — senyum yang menawan hati
anquish — takut, duka cita
to rend-rent-rent — merobek
to writhe — berliuk
to lurch — gerak cepat
to dislodge — mengusir
to stagger — terhuyung-huyung
a corpse — mayat, bangkai
the ranks — barisan
unrestrained — leluasa, tak dikendalikan
jubilant — bersorak-sorai

33. Alengka's Total Defeat

well matched — seimbang
seasoned — berpengalaman
an expert — ahli
to disengage — melepaskan
a vise-like grip — pegangan yang amat kuat
to take to one's heels — melarikan diri, lari
to jeer — mengejek, memperolok-olokkan
to evade — menghindari
a pursuit — pengejaran
tactical withdrawal — kemunduran bersiasat
to incense — membuat marah
a coward — penakut, pengecut
to slay-slew-slain — membunuh
to surrender — menyerah kalah
a fray — pertempuran
a deadliest foe — musuh yang paling berbahaya
within shooting range — dalam daerah penembakan

a counter-attack — serangan pembalasan
to maintain — mempertahankan
to notice — memperhatikan
a jaw — rahang
a trap — perangkap
relentless — tak mengenal belas kasihan
for all his effort — bagaimanapun kuat diusahakan
languished — melemah
doomed — mendapat nasib malang
inhabited — ditempati
to avenge oneself — membalas dendam
mangle — hancur, rusak
an amnesty — pengampunan
to forbid-forbade-forbidden — melarang

34. Happy Ending

invaluable — tak ternilai
to restore — mengembalikan
a misdeed — perbuatan jahat
to smirch — menodai
to be fit for — cocok
an office — jabatan
accordingly — sesuai dengan itu
the benevolent reign — pemerintahan yang baik
happy beyond words — amat berbahagia
re-united — dipertemukan kembali
a reunion — pertemuan kembali
to sustain — mempertahankan diri
to shield — melindungi
an ordeal — kesengsaraan, percobaan berat
appropriate — pantas
to unite — mempersatukan
a marriage — perkawinan
a seal — meterai
to set the seal upon — mempererat
stunningly — mengagumkan
a spouse — isteri, pasangan hidup
the term — batas waktu, masa
to elaps — lalu
in trust — dalam perlindungan

114

to rejoice — bergembira-ria
a procession — arak-arakan
to festoon and to garland — menghias dengan bunga
the affection — kasih sayang
cheering — bersorak-sorai
the weeds — rumput-rumput, semak belukar
to deface — dicemarkan, berobah menjadi
the vestige — bekas, sisa
the poverty — kemiskinan
gentle — lembut, perlahan, jinak
well-behaved — sopan-santun
the quarrels — pertengkaran
enviousness — iri hati
famine — kekurangan, kelaparan
the disease — penyakit
to survive — hidup terus
the goodneighbourliness — hidup bertetangga yang baik
to thrive — berkembang makmur, tumbuh dengan subur
valiant — berani
to cherish — mencintai
to revere — menghormat, memuja
gingerly — berhati-hati
to spin — berputar
the erect position — keadaan tegak
to fall in line with — mengikuti
multifarious — pelbagai macam
to repress — menahan, menindas
to yawn — menguap
to get to ones feet — bangkit berdiri
to adjust — mengatur
a host — tuan rumah
gratitude — perasaan terima kasih
to agree — menyetujui
the stipend — pembayaran
customary — biasa
to take leave — berpisah, berangkat
a sigh of relief — nafas lega
exhausted — menghabiskan tenaga
involuntarily — dengan tak sadar, dengan sendirinya
a sensation of well-being — perasaan puas
glued — melekat
the glue — lem
to illicit — tidak sah

115

guffaw upon guffaw — tertawa terbahak-bahak
to dish up — menghidangkan
a masterful technique — kemahiran yang amat besar
to oppose — melawan, menentang
to owe — berhutang
due to him — berkat dia
incredibly nimble fingers — jari-jari yang luar biasa cepatnya
to accentuate — menitik beratkan
to deserve — patut mendapat
an extensive repertoir — persediaan lagu yang besar
alternatively — berganti-ganti
soul stirring — mengharukan jiwa
to attain — mencapai, mendapat
to interrupt — merintangi, memutus
a narration — cerita
a prevailing mood — suasana yang sedang berada
cardinal — penting, utama
to create — menciptakan, menghasilkan
a span — merentang, meliputi, jangka waktu
infallible — tentu, tak dapat salah
to complaint — mengadu, menuntut
perhaps — barangkali
the latter — akhirnya
to detect — mengetahui, mendapati
to spoil — merusak
the culprit — orang yang salah, orang yang dituduh
precious — berharga
the response — jawaban
an expression — ungkapan
a essential purpose — maksud sesungguhnya
to toy — bermain
to quest — mencari
the significance — arti
human existence — kemanusiaan